A HEURISTIC PROGRAM
FOR ASSEMBLY LINE BALANCING

1960 Award Winner

THE FORD FOUNDATION DOCTORAL DISSERTATION SERIES

A dissertation submitted in partial fulfillment of the requirements for the degree of Doctor of Philosophy at Carnegie Institute of Technology

1959 Award Winners

Kalman J. Cohen
Computer Models of the Shoe, Leather, Hide Sequence
Dissertation submitted to Graduate School of Industrial Administration, Carnegie Institute of Technology

Present Position: Associate Professor of Economics and Industrial Administration, Graduate School of Industrial Administration, Carnegie Institute of Technology

Bob R. Holdren
The Structure of a Retail Market and the Market Behavior of Retail Units
Dissertation submitted to Department of Economics, Yale University

Present Position: Assistant Professor of Economics, Iowa State College, Ames, Iowa

Frank Proschan
Polya Type Distributions in Renewal Theory, with an Application to an Inventory Problem
Dissertation submitted to Department of Statistics, Stanford University

Present Position: Staff Member, Mathematics Laboratory, Boeing Scientific Research Laboratories

Andrew C. Stedry
Budget Control and Cost Behavior
Dissertation submitted to Graduate School of Industrial Administration, Carnegie Institute of Technology

Present Position: Second Lieutenant, United States Army, Operational Mathematics Branch, Research & Engineering Div.

Victor H. Vroom
Some Personality Determinants of the Effects of Participation
Dissertation submitted to Department of Psychology, University of Michigan

Present Position: Assistant Professor of Psychology, University of Pennsylvania

A HEURISTIC PROGRAM FOR ASSEMBLY LINE BALANCING

FRED M. TONGE

1961

P R E N T I C E - H A L L ,   I N C .

Englewood Cliffs, N. J.

To my wife

L. C. Catalog Card Number: **61:11359**

• *Printed in the United States of America*
38694 — C

Foreword

This volume is one of five doctoral dissertations selected for publication in the second annual Doctoral Dissertation Competition sponsored by the Program in Economic Development and Administration of The Ford Foundation. The winning dissertations were completed during the academic year 1959–60 by doctoral candidates in business administration, in the social sciences and other fields relevant to the study of problems of business.

The dissertation competition is intended to generalize standards of excellence in research on business by graduate students. It should give widespread professional recognition to persons recently awarded doctorates in business whose dissertation research is especially distinguished by its analytical content and strong roots in underlying disciplines. It is also intended to give recognition to a selected number of persons outside business schools who in their doctoral dissertations pursued with distinction interests relevant to the field of business.

The dissertations selected include, in addition to Dr. Tonge's monograph:

Decentralization of Authority in a Bureaucracy
        Bernard H. Baum
        Department of Sociology
        University of Chicago

The Distribution of Automobiles:
An Economic Analysis of a Franchise System
        Bedros Peter Pashigian
        Department of Economics
        Massachusetts Institute of Technology

The Choice of Wage Comparisons
        Martin Patchen
        Department of Social Psychology
        University of Michigan

v

Marketing in an Underdeveloped Economy:
The North Indian Sugar Industry
        Leon V. Hirsch
        Graduate School of Business Administration
        Harvard University

In the first year of the competition four of the five dissertations selected made extensive use of mathematical and statistical tools. This may have led some to the mistaken impression that mathematically-oriented dissertations are unduly favored in the selection process. The results of the second year's competition should serve to correct any such misapprehension. Four of the five dissertations published this year are largely non-mathematical, thus underscoring our conviction that many disciplines, including mathematics, can make important contributions to rigorous business research.

On behalf of The Ford Foundation, I wish to express my gratitude to the Editorial Committee for the care and thought its members devoted to the selection process. The same scholars who served on the Committee for the first year's competition gave us the benefit of their experience by serving a second year. They are: Professors Robert Ferber of the University of Illinois, Sherman J. Maisel of the University of California (Berkeley), and William Foote Whyte of Cornell University.

As in the first year, the Editorial Committee's task was considerably lightened by the assistance of ten readers, experts in the wide range of disciplines covered in the Competition, who carefully screened each of the dissertations submitted. The Foundation joins the Committee in acknowledging their debt to Professors Austin C. Hoggatt, Julius Margolis and Lyman W. Porter of the University of California (Berkeley), Richard M. Cyert of the Carnegie Institute of Technology, Harry V. Roberts of the University of Chicago, Frank Miller and Henry Landsberger of Cornell University, Myron J. Gordon of the Massachusetts Institute of Technology, Samuel Goldberg of Oberlin College, and Robert B. Fetter of Yale University, for serving as readers in the second year of the competition.

Finally, my colleagues and I wish to acknowledge the substantial contribution of Prentice-Hall, Inc., to the publication and distribution of the selected dissertations.

                                  Thomas H. Carroll
                                  Vice President
                                  The Ford Foundation

New York, New York
December, 1960

Preface

This volume reports a heuristic program for assembly line balancing. By assembly line balancing we mean the process of assigning jobs to workers stationed along a continuous assembly line. Our goal has not been to develop an optimum procedure for this assignment, but rather to develop an acceptable procedure using certain new problem-solving techniques. These techniques concern both specification of a problem-solving procedure and implementation of that procedure on a digital computer. We have studied assembly line balancing both as an interesting problem in its own right and as representative of a large number of industrial problems to which these techniques have potential application.

Many industrial decisions entail selecting some optimum combination of factors from a space of many possible combinations. Assembly line balancing, job shop scheduling, personnel and equipment assignment are examples of this class of combinatorial problems. Mechanization of solution procedures for such problems can (potentially) contribute not only dollar savings through better solutions for the cost, but also intangible returns through much quicker results. A purpose of this research is to explore one approach to such mechanization.

Because no general theory exists for dealing with large scale combinatorial problems, much basic mathematical research in this area has been directed toward developing computational shortcuts and approximations for treating such problems [see, for example, Dantzig, Fulkerson, and Johnson (7) or Bryton (4)]. In fact, the combinatorial problems listed above are members of the class of ill-structured problems [Simon and Newell (32)]—known exhaustive algorithms for their solution require too much computational effort to be feasible.

The work of Newell, Shaw, and Simon (23) on heuristic problem-solving, although oriented toward human cognitive process rather than industrial decisions, suggests both an approach to combinatorial problems using heuristic procedures and a method of employing electronic computers to carry out these procedures. The research reported here aims to extend these techniques to the solution of the assembly line balancing problem.

Our two goals are: 1. to develop an acceptable, though not necessarily optimum, procedure for assembly balancing, 2. to gain some understanding of the use of computers for implementing heuristic decision procedures in the industrial management area.

The organization of this paper reflects these two goals. The first two chapters provide background information to the assembly line balancing problem. In Chapter 1 we define the line balancing problem in its more general setting of the assembly operation as a whole. In Chapter 2 we view assembly line balancing as a combinatorial problem, examining both general considerations of combinatorial problems and other approaches to the assembly line balancing problem.

Chapters 3 and 4 summarize our assembly line balancing procedure as it presently exists, Chapter 3 describing the procedure and Chapter 4 the results obtained in applying it to several test problems. In Chapter 5 we examine the procedure within a more general framework for problem-solving.

Chapter 6 concerns the philosophy of this approach to using digital computers in dealing with ill-structured problems, drawing upon examples from the line balancing program to illustrate the realization of this approach. In Chapter 7 we present conclusions and extensions of the research to related areas.

The Appendices contain a complete presentation of the actual sample problems used (Appendix A) and the protocols produced by the problem-solving procedure (Appendix B). We also include descriptions in English of the detailed heuristics employed (Appendix C) and of the representation of data within the computer (Appendix D).

The research reported here arose from joint exposure to the assembly line balancing problem in its industrial setting and to the work of Newell, Shaw, and Simon on heuristic programming.

This work has been supported to varying degrees by the Graduate School of Industrial Administration, Carnegie Institute of Technology, an IBM Fellowship, The RAND Corporation, and the Westinghouse Electric Corporation.

Although many people have contributed to developing this topic, the author particularly acknowledges the stimulation and encouragement of A. Newell, J. C. Shaw, and H. Kanter of The RAND Corporation, and H. A. Simon of Carnegie Institute of Technology.

Mrs. Jessie Hausner and Miss Margie Knight provided expert secretarial assistance.

Of course, sole responsibility for content lies with the author.

FRED M. TONGE

Contents

CHAPTER 1

THE ASSEMBLY LINE BALANCING PROBLEM   *1*

1.1.	*Definition of the problem*	*1*
1.2.	*The assembly plant as a decision framework*	*3*
1.3.	*Variables in assembly line balancing*	*5*

CHAPTER 2

COMBINATORIAL ANALYSIS OF THE LINE BALANCING PROBLEM   *8*

2.1.	*Combinatorial problems*	*8*
2.2.	*Magnitude of the line balancing problem*	*9*
2.3.	*Review of the assembly line balancing literature*	*10*

CHAPTER 3

A HEURISTIC PROGRAM FOR ASSEMBLY LINE BALANCING   *16*

3.1.	*Heuristic programs*	*16*
3.2.	*Heuristics for assembly line balancing*	*18*
3.3.	*The assembly line balancing program*	*18*
3.4.	*Constructing the hierarchy of problems (phase I)*	*20*
3.5.	*Grouping tasks into work stations (phase II)*	*24*
3.6.	*Regrouping procedures (modifying the problem tree)*	*26*
3.7.	*Smoothing the resulting balance (phase III)*	*29*
3.8.	*Adding the zoning constraint*	*31*

ix

CHAPTER 4

OPERATING RESULTS WITH THE LINE BALANCING PROGRAM

33

4.1. *Mechanization of the assembly line balancing procedure* 33
4.2. *Operating results* 34
4.3. *Other comparisons* 36

CHAPTER 5

THE ASSEMBLY LINE BALANCING PROGRAM AS A PROBLEM-SOLVING PROCESS

39

5.1. *An abstract model of problem-solving behavior* 39
5.2. *Characteristics of the assembly line balancing problem* 40
5.3. *Exhaustive procedures* 42
5.4. *The heuristic procedure* 43
5.5. *Summary* 46

CHAPTER 6

COMPUTERS AND THE SOLUTION OF ILL-STRUCTURED PROBLEMS

48

6.1. *Problem-solving and computing solutions* 48
6.2. *Characteristics of ill-structured problems* 49
6.3. *Heuristic problem-solving* 50
6.4. *Information processing aspects of ill-structured problems* 50
6.5. *Pre-structuring the problem* 53
6.6. *Another answer to this dilemma* 53
6.7. *Desirable characterisitcs of a language for problem-solving* 54
6.8. *Characteristics of symbol manipulation languages* 54
6.9. *The assembly line balancing problem* 55
6.10. *Mechanizing the assembly line balancing procedure* 56
6.11. *A first evaluation of this project* 58
6.12. *A final remark* 59

CHAPTER 7

IN CONCLUSION

60

7.1.	*Uses of the line balancing program*	*60*
7.2.	*Further development of this program*	*61*
7.3.	*Implications for other combinatorial problems*	*62*
7.4.	*Summary*	*63*

APPENDIX A

SAMPLE PROBLEMS *65*

APPENDIX B

PROTOCOLS OF THE PROBLEM-SOLVING PROCESS *68*

APPENDIX C

DETAILS OF THE ASSEMBLY LINE BALANCING PROCEDURE *99*

APPENDIX D

DATA REPRESENTATION *111*

BIBLIOGRAPHY *113*

CHAPTER 1

The Assembly Line
Balancing Problem

1.1. Definition of the Problem

In many industries (for example, those manufacturing home appliances and automobiles) the product is assembled on a continuous conveyor line. The elemental tasks making up the assembly operation must be assigned to work stations along the line. (For our purposes, 'work station' and 'operator' are equivalent.[1]) In the simplest case, each elemental task (also called 'task' or 'element') is characterized by an operation time per unit of product and a partial ordering relationship with other elemental tasks.

Figure 1 represents one such assembly.[2] Here, for example, elemental task U4 requires five time units. Precedence relationships among elemental tasks are indicated by arrows. Thus, task U4 cannot be started until task U3 is completed, and must be

---

[1] When an elemental task is larger than one work station at the given production rate, it is usually grouped with other elements to form the smallest possible multiple of a work station and processed on one of a set of parallel jigs.

[2] This directed graph representation of the assembly line balancing problem is due to Salveson (30).

completed before either U5 or U21 can be started. The constraint
that task U4 must precede task U6 need not be represented explicitly; this ordering is implied by the sequence U4→U5→U6.

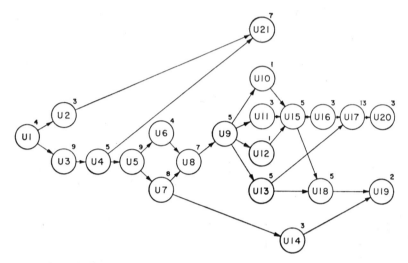

Fig. 1. Twenty-one element problem—directed graph representation

Task U1, the only elemental task having no predecessors, must
be performed first. (U1 might be, for example, the task of moving a chassis from an overhead storage conveyor on to the main
assembly line.) Any one of tasks U19, U20 or U21 could be performed last.

A production rate set by management determines the maximum time (cycle time) to be assigned to any work station. That
is, hours-per-shift divided by units-per-shift determine the maximum time an operator can spend on each unit. Thus, to complete 300 units in a 7.5 hour day, an operator can spend at most
.025 hours-per-unit (the cycle time).

The assembly line balancing problem can be stated as:

> Given a production rate (or, equivalently, a cycle time), what
> is the minimum number of work stations (operators) consist-
> ent with the time and ordering constraints of the product?

More explicitly, the assembly line balancing problem concerns a set of elemental tasks such that:

1. each elemental task requires a known operation time per unit or product, independent of when performed,
2. a partial ordering exists among the elemental tasks.

An optimal solution of the problem consists of an assignment of elemental tasks to work stations such that:

1. each elemental task is assigned to one and only one work station,
2. the sum of the times of all elemental tasks assigned to any one station does not exceed some maximum (the cycle time),
3. the stations thus formed can be ordered such that the partial orderings among elemental tasks are not violated,
4. the number of work stations thus formed is minimized.

An optimal solution to the problem of Figure 1 for a cycle time of 20 is given in Figure 6.

In most instances the ordering constraints are not explicitly stated. The industrial engineer balancing a line works from a sheet listing the elements and their operation times and from his knowledge of the manufacturing process. In the absence of any formal procedures, he must rely on judicious use of trial-and-error methods to find an acceptable grouping.

1.2. The Assembly Plant as a Decision Framework

The industrial setting of line balancing is the assembly plant as a whole. Within this setting, balancing the assembly line is one of many decisions to be made and remade. Let us examine how solutions of the line balancing problem interact with other decisions.

The over-all company production decision is influenced by demand estimates, estimates of the amount of product in the distribution system and estimates of the cost of unfilled orders, and the 'scrap' value of overproduction. From these factors a firm demand for product over time is synthesized. Production management strives to meet that demand at minimum cost. Indeed, in general, there is a set of demands for different products over time, each competing for a share of scarce company resources.

Major factors to be considered in any assembly plant decision-making scheme include raw materials procurement and inventories, fabrication (feeder) operations, finished component inventories and material handling systems, subassembly lines with associated inventories and material handling systems, final assembly, and finished goods inventories. In some of these areas the various product demands must be considered jointly; in others they may be taken separately.

Various authors [see Whitin (36), Salveson (30), Kwo (15) as examples] have examined in detail the necessary decisions in each of these areas. We do not propose to study the entire complex system of factory scheduling, or even the relation of each of these decisions to something we call "the assembly line balancing problem." We must recognize, however, the industrial situation in which our assembly line balancing problem arises.

These factors are interrelated; decisions about any one has repercussions for the others. For example [Kwo (15)], the actual rate at which an assembly line can be operated and the component inventories necessary to support that operation depend on the efficiency of the conveyor system linking the assembly area with feeder operations. In turn, that efficiency (and thus the actual rate) is dependent on the scheduled operation rates of the assembly line and feeder operations.

Usual decision-making practice is to set a completion schedule for each product and gear activity in all areas to meet that schedule, making such adjustments in the production rate as may be necessary due to bottlenecks. Then, given a production rate apparently feasible for all supporting activities, the final assembly line is balanced to that rate. Because the feasibility of this rate generally is marginal for one or more of the supporting activities, and because product demand estimates are subject to continual revision by actual sales experience, the production rate is changed and the line rebalanced with unscheduled regularity.

Salveson (30) stresses the economic desirability of a method to *"compute optimum balances for assembly lines for many different levels of output in advance and thereby permit reduction by two to three weeks [of] the lead time required to change the rate of production when required by changes in sales."*

This usual decision scheme reflects a precise production rate "handed down from above" for each product. We can envision alternative approaches to determining a final assembly rate. One might ask what are the best production rates for the various products to be produced concurrently, given the available manpower. To answer this question we need actual line balances at different production rates, since the function relating number of workers to units produced is discontinuous.

1.3. Variables in Assembly Line Balancing

Let us now consider the assembly line balancing problem independent of decisions in other areas. Several variables are present in the problem in its natural state. We examine and make assumptions about each in turn.

The product to be assembled is characterized by time requirements for each final assembly task and by restrictions on the way these tasks may be grouped into work stations. These grouping restrictions are either ordering constraints, stating which tasks must be completed before other tasks can be started, or zoning constraints, specifying which tasks may not be grouped together because of the production facility layout. The requirement of completing all work inside the product before fastening on the top cover is an ordering constraint. The injunction against assigning tasks to be done from both the front and the back of the product to one worker, thus requiring him to cross the conveyor line, is a zoning constraint. Initially we consider only ordering constraints. The effect of the zoning constraints is introduced later in our analysis.

Choosing a particular work method for a product, thus determining the ordering and zoning constraints, is an interesting problem in itself, but is not treated here. We take the work method as given. Likewise, we assume a given set of elemental tasks which cannot be further subdivided.

The time requirement for each task is not a constant, but varies both with different workers and with repeated performance by the same worker. This requirement might be represented as a random draw from some empirically determined distribution. In actual industrial practice, a single value—typically derived from standard time data—is generally used. The usual questions of the additivity of these times can be raised [see, for example, Buffa (3)], but for this research we assume a constant time for each task. It can be claimed that the various allowances and margins incorporated in the time values at least compensate for variability in operation times or inconsistencies due to non-additivity. Some firms reportedly never balance to more than, say, 90 per cent of a work load (including allowances) because "the men won't take it."

Labor skill requirements may vary with the different assembly tasks, so that various groupings of tasks may require more or fewer high rate workers, affecting the cost per unit of product. We assume for this first analysis that wage rates are independent of the tasks being performed. Also we ignore the effects of worker learning on the productive capacity of the line.

The usual criterion for line balancing is minimization of the number of workers required to meet a given production rate. However, we seek a satisfactory rather than optimal line balance. At the same time, we attempt to equalize the distribution of work load among stations, increasing the potential production rate from a given number of men and reducing the likelihood of unrest due to unequal work loads. (The manner in which these criteria are implemented is presented in Chapter 3.)

In summary, the assembly line balancing problem considered here concerns a product assembled by performing a number of elemental tasks, each task characterized by a time required per unit of product and a partial ordering with other tasks. The problem is to assign these tasks to work stations (workers) along the assembly line so that a given production rate is met, the number of stations is satisfactorily small, and the amount of work assigned to the various stations is as even as possible.

CHAPTER 2

Combinatorial Analysis
of the Line Balancing Problem

2.1. Combinatorial Problems

Assembly line balancing is representative of a class of combinatorial problems in which elements of a set are to be ordered or grouped according to some criterion. Other examples of such problems are plentiful. In machine shop scheduling, a sequence of jobs through machines is chosen to minimize time beyond due date. In the traveling salesman problem, a route must be picked which covers all points and minimizes total distance traveled. Personnel and equipment assignment requires that these factors be allocated so as to minimize the cost of completing all jobs on schedule. In assembly line balancing there must be selected, from all acceptable groupings of elemental tasks into stations, a grouping that meets, with a minimum number of stations, the restrictions of technological precedence and a given production rate.

Combinatorial problems might be characterized by the existence in most cases of a simply stated algorithm (computational procedure) for enumerating all possible solutions, and by a factorial growth in the amount of computation required to carry out that enumeration as problem size increases. (There are $n!$ possible orderings of n cities along a route, $n!$ possible assignments of n men to n distinct jobs, and so forth.) Since a problem involving 100 elements generates $100! = 3 \times 10^{157}$ distinct orderings—a task requiring 3×10^{114} years if 1,000,000 orderings can be produced and examined a second—simple, brute forces approaches are not feasible for problems of any size.

Several sophisticated mathematical techniques have been evolved which are suitable for dealing with problems of this nature. Foremost of these are linear programming and dynamic programming. For particular problems it is possible to develop enumerative methods that tend to produce satisfactory answers. In some cases it is even possible to find methods guaranteeing an optimum solution with a reasonable amount of computation. In the following we shall review published attempts to apply these methods to the assembly line balancing problem.

2.2. Magnitude of the Line Balancing Problem

It is fashionable in discussing combinatorial problems to point out the magnitude of performing an exhaustive analysis of the problem at hand. It would seem desirable to produce some such measure as a benchmark for the line balancing problem.

The obvious estimate of $n!$ possible orderings for a problem on n elements is too gross, as the precedence constraints dictate that any reasonable method consider only feasible orderings. (In the sample problems included in this study, the "average" element could be grouped directly preceding or following one-third of the other elements in the problem.) An estimate of the number of feasible orderings is difficult to make, but a program on a medium speed digital computer (with tapes) was prepared at the Westinghouse Research Laboratories to generate all such orderings. The program took 200 times as long to process a twenty-one element problem as to process a ten element problem.

The extrapolation of this increase to the 70–100 element problems found in industrial practice must be extremely large.

Salveson (30) points out that assembly line balancing can and should be treated as a problem in combinations rather than permutations, thus reducing the number of possible groupings for a 100 element problem to (his estimate) $\sim 76 \times 10^4$. The sample problems considered in this report indicate an average of three rather than five elements per station for typical production rates, thus predicting $\sim 15 \times 10^4$ groupings. However, this estimate also ignores the effect of precedence constraints.

Numerous facts can be derived from the structure of the problems considered here. However, attempts at constructing an accurate numerical formulation of the number of choices at each step in an exhaustive approach have not succeeded. Actual machine effort comparisons between the heuristic program presented here and a particular exhaustive algorithm [due to Jackson (16)] are presented in Chapter 4.

2.3. Review of the Assembly Line Balancing Literature

Salveson (30) produced the first published management science study of the assembly line balancing problem. His article contains many useful insights into the relation between the assembly line balancing problem as it exists in an industrial operation and the abstraction necessary for application of mathematical techniques. But the computational techniques he suggests are stated so vaguely that complete evaluation of their usefulness is impossible, and such evaluation as is possible indicates that they require too much effort to be practical.

Salveson begins by pointing out that one could enumerate all possible work stations and then use linear programming to choose the combination of work stations that best meets the requirements placed on a solution. He notes, however, that the use of linear programming would require the inversion of an extremely large matrix, and so would, in realistic problems, be computationally unfeasible. He then suggests that in lieu of a matrix inversion *"we endeavor to have this method take advantage of the alert characteristics of the human mind in handling combinatorial problems of reasonable proportions."* That is, he proposes to substitute combinatorial analysis for the matrix inversion. This analysis would consist of removing some potential station or set of stations from an acceptable solution and replacing them with another set giving minimum idle time for the particular tasks involved.

Salveson's suggested procedure can be summarized as:

1. Enumerate all possible stations,
2. Generate a feasible grouping,
3. Attempt regrouping using combinatorial analysis.

The major objections to this method (raised by discussant S. Johnson) are:

1. Enumeration of all possible work stations for a practical sized problem is an enormous task.

2. The method for choosing the set of stations to be removed and subjected to combinatorial analysis is not specified. (Salveson does point out that unless the sum of idle times for the set is greater than the maximum station time allowable, no reduction in the number of stations can be expected.)

3. The effort required to find the set of stations with minimum idle time including a given set of elements, although clearly smaller than the line balancing problem as a whole, may be extremely large in actual industrial problems.

We must note that the linear programming formulation suggested by Salveson is incomplete and allows unacceptable sets of stations to be formed. Also, the application of linear programming techniques known at the time of his article would not in general have resulted in useable solutions but would have produced answers with fractional work stations. The recent work of Gomory (11) and others on integer programming has made solution of this and many other management science problems theoretically possible, although as yet computationally unfeasible.

G. Dantzig has suggested (to the author) another linear programming formulation of the assembly line balancing problem. This formulation accounts for the links (ordering constraints) between elemental tasks, and so can be derived easily from the initial statement of the problem. However, for a problem with k elements, l links, and m maximum number of stations, the formulation requires about $k + m + l(m - 1)$ equations in $km + l(m - 1)$ unknowns, an enormous system for practical sized problems. Again, integer programming techniques are required to produce a non-fractional answer.

Bowman (2) has suggested two integer linear programming formulations of the line balancing problem. One is essentially identical to that of Dantzig. The second, which is quite similar to the usual linear programming formulation of job shop scheduling, views the problem as one of packing the elements into fixed work stations (or time intervals). For a problem with k elements, l orderings, m maximum number of stations, and n mutually unordered pairs of elements, this formulation requires about $2k + l + 3n$ equations in $2k + n$ unknowns.

In an unpublished thesis predating Salveson's work, Bryton (4) presents a "convergence" procedure for assembly line balancing. Bryton considers the problem of finding minimum unproductive time for a given number of stations, that is, varying the cycle time (and consequently the production rate) to minimize idle time for a given number of stations. The procedure consists of interchanging, between the largest and smallest stations, the pair of elements whose difference in time requirements is nearest to one-half the difference between the stations, and repeating this procedure until no more improvement is attained. Then, either the resulting balance is accepted as the final solution, or an arbitrary transfer is made to unbalance the situation and the procedure repeated.

As Bryton points out, the procedure would be improved if more than one element from each station were considered, but he feels the complexity introduced would make the procedure too complicated to be used.

Although the constant number of work stations problem is not the one being considered in this book, it is the problem of "smoothing" the balance once one has been found for a given production rate. Bryton's techniques are quite similar to our trading procedure, the primary heuristic employed in the "smoothing" phase of the heuristic program.

The major objections to this method as a direct approach to large problems are:

1. It considers only transfers of a single element from each station rather than several elements,
2. In large problems the simple concept of each transfer causing improvement is insufficient.

It is sometimes necessary to plan sequences of transfers, some of which result in an intermediately worse balance, to reach an improved final balance. In Bryton's system this is left to the chance step of arbitrarily unbalancing the solution and restarting the convergence procedure.

J. R. Jackson (16) has developed a computational procedure for the line balancing problem, using exhaustive enumeration. The method consists of enumerating all possible first stations, for each first station enumerating all possible second stations, and so forth. Rules are given for eliminating one of two sequences of stations containing the same elements, and for eliminating that one of the otherwise identical stations which contains the smaller of parallel elements.

Proofs are given that the method is exhaustive and that it will therefore find the optimal solution. The only possible objection to this method is the computational effort involved. In his article, Jackson speaks of having used the method successfully by hand on problems of up to 100 elements. However, these are synthetic problems containing relatively many more ordering constraints than our seventy element problem (Figure A3). The

Jackson procedure is used in our heuristic program as a "last ditch" method. A comparison of its performance with that of the heuristic program as a whole is found in Chapter 4.

J. Mitchell (20) has extended the theoretical statement of Jackson's algorithm to include the zoning constraint mentioned previously. Also, Helgeson and Kwo (13) have commented on expanding Jackson's criteria of an acceptable balance to include an even distribution of work among stations.

Dynamic programming should be considered as a method for assembly line balancing. No application of this technique has been made to the line balancing problem as stated here. The assembly line problems treated by Bellman (1) and Pollack (29) are, in fact, the classical machine sequencing problem of Johnson (17) that includes inventory accumulation between machines. However, the problems are similar enough that they suggest a somewhat different way of viewing assembly line balancing.

Bellman considers i items to be processed through k machines, all in the same sequence, with storages before each machine. He derives the recurrence relations describing the delay of each item at each machine. The functional equation approach of dynamic programming can then be used to find that sequence of items which minimizes total elapsed time or some other suitable function of the sequence. Our line balancing problem differs in that there are no storages, and the items are homogeneous. Since the items are homogeneous, we can consider the delay before each machine (which in the steady state is the same for every item) as part of the machining time. Then the problem we wish to solve can be stated as: Given a set of tasks, how do we define machines (i.e., group the tasks into work stations) so that for a given production rate the idle times of the machines (analogous to the delay times of Bellman's formulation) are minimized. This recurrence equation approach to line balancing will not be developed any further here.

Hoffman (14) presents a computational technique, using precedence matrices, for generating technologically acceptable groupings of elements. The reference mentions the possible application of this technique to the assembly line balancing problem. Bryton (4) also develops some interesting techniques for using precedence matrices in determining the possibility of combining certain elements.

Helgeson and Bernie (12) suggest the use of "ranked positional weights" in choosing which elements to consider next in grouping into work stations. An element's weight is the sum of its time plus the times of those elements which, because of the precedence relationships, cannot be performed until it is performed. (For example, the positional weight of elemental task U15 in Figure 1 is 31.) While this method does not guarantee the best solution, it requires relatively little computing effort. A comparison of the method's performance with that of the heuristic procedure is given in Chapter 4.

Scott (31) considers the industrial setting of the line balancing problem and evaluates several proposed methods of solution. Texts by Churchman, Arnoff, and Ackoff (5) and Vasonyi (34) also mention the problem and some of the above-mentioned work, though generally without any critical evaluation.

The exhaustive methods cited above fall short as computational procedures because the methods they use to reduce the number of possibilities considered are not selective enough overall. An approach that concentrates effort on those parts of the problem which seemed to require it, rather than indiscriminately spinning out and eliminating possibilities at all stages of the solution process, would seem to be, a priori, a more feasible problem-solving procedure.

CHAPTER 3

A Heuristic Program
for Assembly Line Balancing

3.1. Heuristic Programs

Webster's *New International Dictionary of the English Language*, 1959, defines the adjective "heuristic" as "serving to discover or reveal." Thus, by heuristics we mean [after Newell and Simon (25)] principles or devices that contribute, on the average, to the reduction of search in problem-solving activity. The admonitions "draw a diagram" in geometry, "reduce everthing to sines and cosines" in proving trigonometric identities, or "always take a check—it may be mate" in chess are all familiar heuristics.

Heuristic problem-solving procedures are procedures organized around such effort-saving devices. A heuristic program is the mechanization on a digital computer of some heuristic procedure. The computer attempts to solve the problem by carrying out the heuristic program. At present this use of digital computers is the only means we have of making explicit the behavior of a complex heuristic procedure in dealing with a large class of problems. The Logic Theorist (25), the Chess Machine (22), and the Geometry Machine (8) are examples of working heuristic programs in other areas.

The distinction between heuristic and non-heuristic problem-solving procedures is often vague. Rather than attempt to specify a rule by which all procedures can be so categorized, we shall cite some common characteristics of existing heuristic procedures:

1. Factorization of the problem into a number of "smaller" problems and subproblems (often through means-end analysis), with a corresponding goal-subgoal organization of behavior. For example, the Chess Machine might realize that it cannot play P-K4 because it would lose an exchange on that square, and, consequently, it would set up the subgoal of first bringing another man to bear on its K4.

2. Use of cues in the environment to determine the particular behavior evoked from a wide set of possible alternatives available to the program, that is, a high degree of interdependence between the specific problem (from a more general class) being considered and the particular problem-solving methods used. Thus, the methods used by the assembly line balancing program for choosing elements to shift between groupings depend on the particular characteristics of those groupings.

3. Use of recursive procedures to bring to bear on sub-problems the same repertoire of problem-solving techniques used on the original problem. Thus, the Logic Theorist can use the same "bag of tricks" to prove a derived expression as to prove the initial statement from which the derived expression was produced.

4. No guarantee of a satisfactory solution or, often, of any solution. For example, the Chess Machine, because of time and space limitations, may not be able to consider some promising continuations, including the a posteriori optimum one.

Because a heuristic procedure substitutes the effort-reduction of its short cuts for the guaranteed optimal solution of an exhaustive method, the justification of such a program as a problem solver must be in terms of the number of cases successfully solved and the relative amount of effort involved. In a later chapter on operating results the assembly balancing program presented here is compared with several exhaustive procedures.

3.2. Heuristics for Assembly Line Balancing

The set of heuristics outlined here for balancing an assembly line evolved from several sources: discussions with industrial engineers of how they actually balance lines; study of the various papers cited above; explorations with several co-workers, particularly A. Newell, of possible techniques; and, finally, extensive experimentation with particular instances of the problem.[1]

3.3. The Assembly Line Balancing Program

This heuristic approach to assembly line balancing is based on simplification of a complex combinatorial problem until it becomes solvable (in most cases) by simple, straight-forward methods.

Two recursively defined routines form the essence of this procedure. Phase I constructs a hierarchy of increasingly simpler line balancing problems by aggregating groups of elements into a single compound element. Each of these compound elements is in itself a member of this same class of line balancing problems, since it is made up of elements requiring a given operation time and among whom partial ordering relationships exist.

Phase II solves a simple (small number of elements) line balancing problem by assigning groups of available workmen to elements and then taking as subproblems those compound ele-

---

[1] Several other strategies could be suggested as bases for heuristic approches to the problem, although we will do no more than mention them. 1. Divide the problem into relatively independent subproblems, solve each of these by optimizing techniques, and combine the sub-solutions by heuristic methods. 2. Abstract a problem from the original by replacing all times with one of a single large or a single small value, solve that problem, and then adjust the result to fit actual times. 3. Develop stations in an order determined by the density of partial ordering constraints, first building in those regions of the problem where there is least freedom among elements. 4. Assign the n men that, by some estimate, are needed to balance the line at this cycle time to the n largest elements, then group the smaller elements in with these to reach a satisfactory balance.

ments (simple problems in themselves) which have been assigned to more than one man.

This approach requires heuristics for aggregating groups of elements into compound elements, for solving the simplified problems thus created, and for re-introducing the detail of the original problem when the simplified version does not yield a solution.

A third phase of the problem-solving process, utilizing virtually the same heuristics as already required, involves "smoothing" the final work load (assigned time) among work stations. Since the greatest total time assigned any work station limits the speed of the line, a smooth balance answers the problem, "What is the highest production rate achievable with a given number of men? That is, since both men and time are measured in discrete units, a *non-smoothed* optimum solution of the problem, "given a production rate, minimize the number of men required," need not be an optimum solution of the dual problem, "given a number of men, maximize the production rate."

In summary, the general problem-solving scheme calls for:

Phase I. Repeated application of aggregative procedures, creating a hierarchy of simplified line balancing problems ranging in complexity from the initial problem to one containing a single compound element.

Phase II. Recursive application to these simplified problems of a procedure for assigning men to tasks, down to the level of problems whose component tasks require one man each. When the compound elements making up a problem require more men than are available, these elements are broken up and their components regrouped to require fewer men.

Phase III. Smoothing the resulting balance by transferring tasks among work stations until the distribution of assigned time is as even as possible.

The following sections discuss the heuristics entailed in each of these procedures. We use the twenty-one element problem, shown in Figure 1, as an example in this discussion.

Since this approach does not guarantee an optimum solution to the over-all line balancing problem, we must have some notion of a satisfactory solution and accept or reject proposed solutions based on this notion. Also, since the solution of a problem does not guarantee that its subproblems will be solved, whatever process generates solutions must remain active until all sub-problems have been solved, ready to generate another solution if necessary. The methods by which these requirements are met are indicated below.

3.4. Constructing the Hierarchy of Problems (Phase I)

The ordering constraints present in the problem suggest two natural units of aggregation of elements. Either a completely ordered relationship exists between several elements, for example, U3 must always precede U4 (Figure 1), or no ordering is specified, for example, U10, U11, U12. We adopt the 'chain' and the 'set' as basic aggregative units in constructing a simplified problem:

1. A group of adjacent elements whose relative order is completely determined, each except the first having a single direct predecessor and each except the last having a single direct follower, can be replaced by a single compound element, called a *chain.*

2. A group of elements whose relative order is completely unspecified, all having the same direct predecessors and followers, can be replaced by a single compound element, called a *set.*

Thus, U10, U11, U12 in Figure 1 can be replaced by a set 'V2', and then V2, U15 can be replaced by a chain 'V3'. These aggregations can be indicated on the original problem, as shown in Figure 2a. However, it is convenient to represent the aggregations as a branching tree, with each compound element having beneath it the elements of which it is composed. The tree of compound element V3 is shown in Figure 2b. Note that the time requirement of a compound element is the sum of the times of its components.

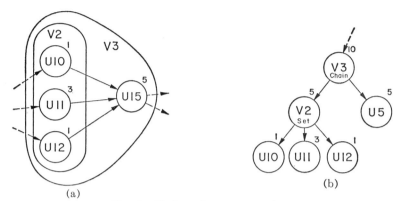

(a)   (b)

Fig. 2. Chain and set aggregations

We use the term 'chain relationship' to indicate that some ordering (possibly indirect) exists between two elements and 'set relationship' to indicate that none exists.

Although the solution strategy calls for repeated application of these aggregative operations to yield a hierarchy of simplified problems, these two types of aggregation are not sufficient to reduce most actual problems completely (to a single compound element). We can proceed first by defining more complex aggregative operations and then, if necessary, by moving "troublesome" ordering constraints. Proposed solutions must then be checked to see that these missing constraints are not violated.

The one additional compound element introduced to date is the 'Z'.

3. A *Z* is a group of four elements with the two front elements having common predecessors and the other two back elements having common followers. The single direct follower of one front element is one of the back elements; the two direct followers of the other front element are the back elements. The back elements have no other direct predecessors.

An example of a *Z* and its representation in tree form is given in Figures 3a and 3b. (Note that there is a prescribed canonical order of subelements in the tree representation of the chain and the Z.)

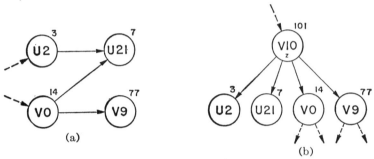

Fig. 3. Z aggregations

The recursive procedure carrying out this aggregating process may be applied to any assemblage of elements. By an assemblage of elements we mean those given elements without predecessors within the assemblage (called the front elements) and their direct followers, and their followers' direct followers, and so forth, to and including those elements with no direct followers (called the back elements). The twenty-one element problem of Figure 1 is an assemblage with front element U1.

While we do not present here the full details of this procedure, a brief summary follows.

Given an assemblage of elements with a single front element, the routine attempts to create a chain. When an element having several direct followers is encountered, the routine first sets up the subproblem of aggregating those several front elements into a single element and then applies itself to that subproblem. (The routine is recursive, so that attempting to solve that subproblem may involve setting up and attempting to solve sub-subproblems and so forth.) If the subproblem is solved successfully, the higher level problem of creating a chain is continued. If the subproblem fails, or if an element is encountered with direct predecessors outside the assemblage (other than those of the front element), the higher level problem fails.

Given an assemblage of elements with several front elements, the routine attempts to create a set or, failing that, a Z. If this can be done, the problem becomes one of reducing an assemblage with a single front element. If not, the routine first sets up the independent subproblems of aggregating separate assemblages starting with each of the front elements, and applies itself to each of these subproblems in turn. When these subproblems are concluded, the higher level problem of creating a set or Z is resumed.

Trying to resolve these subproblems independently often re-

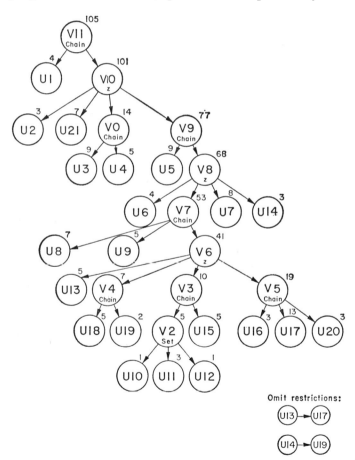

Fig. 4. Twenty-one element problem—Phase I output

veals complex ordering constraints between them. A Z is then postulated incorporating such constraints. Further constraints that prevent completion of an already postulated Z are relaxed so that the Z can be completed, and the higher level problem is then continued.

Figure 4 is the tree of compound elements constructed by application of this recursive procedure to the problem of Figure 1. The running commentary of this program is included in Appendix B; as "Phase I—Twenty-one Element Problem." This is a dynamic statement of how the program is proceeding. It is instructive to follow through this "protocol" while viewing Figures 1 and 4. This first phase of the problem-solving process need be carried out only once for a given product (set of constraints). The resulting hierarchy is supplied as an input to the second phase of the process.

3.5. Grouping Tasks into Work Stations (Phase II)

Inputs to the second phase, grouping tasks into work stations, are: the problem hierarchy as developed in Phase I, a cycle time determined by the required production rate, and a 'per cent usable time' supplied as a guide for setting up and accepting potential work stations. Per cent usable time is an estimate (at present made by the user) of how close to the required station time the task elements can be grouped. This measure reflects the structure and time values of the particular problem being solved. For example, given a cycle time of twenty and a per cent usable time of 90 per cent, the routine will try to construct work stations with an average time of eighteen. (The use of per cent usable time is discussed in more detail in Appendix C.)

The assignment routine consists of a simple recursive procedure for allocating men (work stations) to groups of tasks and a set of procedures for regrouping the tasks (modifying the tree) when necessary. These regrouping heuristics are described in the following section.

The recursive routine for allocating men to groups of tasks proceeds as follows:

1. An initial estimate is made of the number of men required to meet the given production rate, given a per cent usable time (per cent effectiveness). This number of men is assigned to the 'top' compound element, representing a single grouping of all task elements. The recursive routine described in step 2 is then applied to that element. If the routine succeeds, the line has been balanced, and Phase II ends. If the routine fails, the number of men assigned to the top element is increased and the procedure repeated.

2a. If the element being considered has been assigned more than one man, these available men are allocated among the direct components of the element according to their time requirements. This recursive routine is then applied to each of these component elements in turn. If the routine successfully solves each of the subproblems, then the problem of grouping tasks into work stations is also solved at this level, and the routine terminates. If the available men cannot be allocated among the direct components of the element in question—if, considered independently, they require more men than are available—then regrouping procedures are called upon to shift tasks among these groupings so that they are independently solvable. If such a regrouping cannot be found, control is returned to the next higher level, signalling failure to solve the subproblem.

If the recursive routine should fail to handle one of the components below this level and report back failure, excess elements from the failing subproblem are shifted to another grouping or, failing that, the regrouping procedures are activated to produce another set of independent groupings. Again, if solvable subproblems cannot be found, control is returned to the next higher level with a failure signal.

2b. If the element being considered has been assigned a single man, additional elements are added to it if necessary to bring it near the maximum allowable size, and the grouping is marked as a work station. Control then returns to the next higher level, signalling success.

Thus, this recursive routine, like that of Phase I, deals with examples of a particular class of problems (line balancing problems). It solves a problem by setting up within it (and solving in the same way) other 'easier' problems of the same class whose solutions can be combined to solve the larger problem also. In particular, Phase I of this program makes use of natural groupings of the elemental tasks to build up a hierarchy of simplified problems, and Phase II attempts to balance the line using these groupings as complete units, transfering tasks among these groupings only when the simple allocation scheme fails.

3.6. Regrouping Procedures (Modifying the Problem Tree)

Five regrouping procedures: direct transfer, trading, sequential grouping, complete grouping, and exhaustive grouping are available to the Phase II recursive routine when its simple scheme for allocating available men fails. Which of these regrouping heuristics will be called upon, and in what order, is determined by characteristics of the compound elements being regrouped. These procedures are also used by Phase III of the assembly line balancing program in smoothing a proposed line balance.

All five methods make use of a single recursive routine that scans a given part of the hierarchy of elements (the problem tree) and generates a sequence of groups of elements lying within certain specifications (maximum total time of group and minimum total time of group, from front or from back). This routine proceeds by building a first group, always taking the largest element acceptable, and then constructs further groups by eliminating from consideration (or breaking down into components, if a compound element) successive elements of that first group and applying itself to the remaining elements of the given part of the hierarchy. For example, if requested to produce groups totaling at least eight but not more than 16 time units from the back of compound element V6 (see Figure 4), the routine would generate the sequence [(V5, U13, U20), (U20, U17)]. The routine generates each element of this sequence as requested, remembering where it is in the sequence so that it can generate the next one.

The first three methods: direct transfer, trading, and sequential grouping are used to set up independently solvable subproblems which can then be handled by the Phase II recursive routine.

> *Direct Transfer* is applied when only two components are involved. This method tries simply to transfer elements from one component to the other and thus reduce the number of men required by a straightforward totaling of whole men.

For example, if V11 in Figure 4 had been assigned six men (given a cycle time of twenty), the direct transfer procedure would first attempt to shift elements totaling at least one but not more than sixteen time units from V10 to U1, and would, in fact, shift V0 (14 time units).

> *Trading* also applies only to two components, and assumes that direct transfer has been attempted without success. Trading tries to regroup by shifting an element larger than the acceptable limit from one component in exchange for smaller elements (in a set relationship with the first element shifted) from the other component.

An example of this method is cited in the next section.

> *Sequential Grouping* is used when there are several components, and attempts to construct an acceptable work station from the front of the given group of components. If the remaining components can be handled by the remaining men available, the method is considered successful. If not, an attempt is made to construct another work station from the back of the component group, and a similar test is made.

Suppose, for example, that V7 in Figure 4 had been assigned three men (cycle time twenty). Since V7 is made up of three components requiring one, one, and three men, regrouping procedures would be evoked. Sequential grouping would first group together U8, U9, and V2. Since the remaining component V6 would now total thirty-six time units, requiring only the two remaining available men, the method would be successful.

The remaining two regrouping procedures, complete grouping and exhaustive grouping, try to solve completely the subproblems remaining. They may be regarded as "last ditch" methods.

> *Complete Grouping* attempts, first from the front of the component group and then from the back, to construct work stations until all task elements are grouped. If at any time the method cannot construct a station such that the remaining elements total less than can be handled by the remaining men, the method fails.

> *Exhaustive Grouping* generates all possible (independent) first work stations, then all possible following work stations for each of these. This method is the exhaustive algorithm suggested by Jackson (16). Because of the comparatively large amount of effort required to do an exhaustive grouping, this procedure is used only when two men are to be assigned. The method does furnish to the next higher level Phase II routine (on failure) the best groupings it was able to construct from the front and the back, as well as which elements were left ungrouped in those solutions.

Although these regrouping methods are clearly not foolproof, they have proven satisfactory for all problems attempted to date. Figure 5 shows the problem of Figures 1 and 4 after the Phase II recursive routine has been applied to it (cycle time, twenty, 90 per cent usable time), and Figure 6 pictures the work stations thus created on the original problem.

Appendix B contains the protocol produced during this assignment, labelled "Phase II—Twenty-one Element Problem—Cycle Time Twenty—Per Cent Usable Ninety."

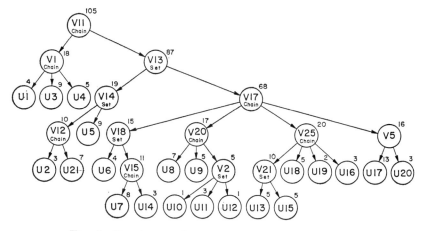

Fig. 5. Twenty-one element problem—Phase II output

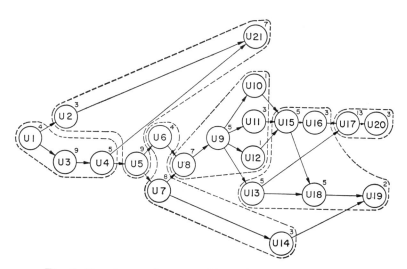

Fig. 6. Twenty-one element problem with stations, cycle time
twenty

3.7. Smoothing the Resulting Balance (Phase III)

Phase III of the assembly line balancing program seeks to
even the distribution of work among work stations by repeatedly
reducing the time requirement of the largest work station. In-

puts to this phase of the problem are a balanced line in hierarchical representation, such as would be produced by Phase II, and a cycle time. This iterative routine uses the same regrouping heuristics used by the Phase II recursive routine.

The following steps comprise the Phase III procedure:

1. Calculate the least possible time value of the highest station (with the given cycle time). If the largest station's time value is not greater than this bound, no further smoothing is possible, and the routine terminates.

2. Given the largest station, consider in turn, in increasing order of size, all "adjacent" (in a set relationship or direct predecessors or followers) stations to that largest station. Try to even the distribution of work between them using the direct transfer heuristic. If successful, return to step 1. If not, go to step 3.

3. Consider again those stations adjacent to the largest station in increasing order of size. Try to reduce the work load of the larger, using the trading heuristic. If successful, return to step 1. If not, proceed to step 4.

4. Once again, consider adjacent stations in increasing order of size. For each one, using first direct transfer and then trading, try to make any transfer that reduces the largest station, even if the formerly smaller station is now as large or larger. If some such transfer is found, set up the subproblem of reducing this new larger station, and apply this routine to it (except that step 4, setting up further subproblems, cannot be used). If successful, return to step 1; if not, the Phase III routine terminates.

The procedure outlined above has not yet been coded (which should be a relatively easy task as it relies heavily on already-coded routines), but it has been hand-simulated for several cases. The result of this hand-simulation for the problem of Figures 1 and 4 is shown in Figure 7. The simulated output of this phase of the assembly line balancing program is given in Appendix B, labelled "Phase III—Twenty-one Element Problem—Cycle Time Twenty—Per Cent Usable Ninety."

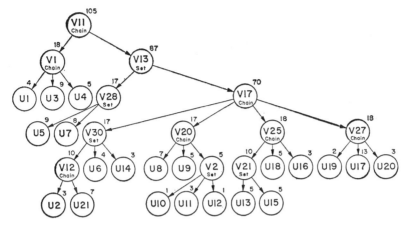

Fig. 7. Twenty-one element problem—Phase III output

3.8. Adding the Zoning Constraint

One of the advantages sought from the heuristic approach to complex decision problems is the ability to redefine the problem, adding or deleting restrictions on a solution, with ease. As a specific example, we introduce the zoning restriction treated by Mitchell (20). Under this restriction each elemental task is assigned to one or more zones reflecting the physical limitations of the production process.

To incorporate this new restriction, the basic grouping generator (see *Regrouping Procedures*) is modified to produce only groupings within a specified zone or zones, and the routine that accepts work stations is modified to reject groups whose elements are not in a common zone. These modifications can be made relatively easily without affecting other parts of the over-all program. These modifications have been hand-simulated for several problems. Table A1 indicates the zoning of elements in the sample problem of Figure 1. Figure 8 shows the result of the modified Phase II operation on that problem (cycle time twenty).

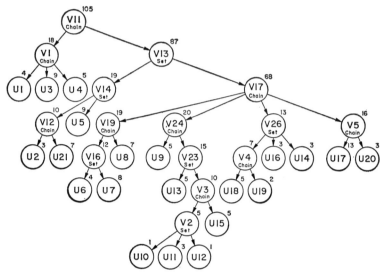

Fig. 8. Twenty-one element problem with zoning constraint—
Phase II output

CHAPTER 4

Operating Results with
the Line Balancing Program

4.1. Mechanization of the Assembly Line Balancing Procedure

Phases I and II of the assembly line balancing procedure described here are programmed in an interpretive system, IPL-IV (Information Processing Language IV), on The RAND Corporation's digital computer JOHNNIAC. The IPL system uses about 1200 of the JOHNNIAC's 4096 words of high-speed core storage and about 650 words of the 12,288 word auxiliary drum storage. In running the line balancing program, which makes heavy use of the drum for temporary storage of data, the system interprets at the rate of about 9,500 IPL instructions per minute. Although there has been no published account of IPL-IV, the closely related IPL-V for the IBM 650, 704, 709, and 7090 is fully documented (25, 26, 27).

The assembly line balancing program itself requires about 6700 machine locations, of which about 6100 are in auxiliary storage. A detailed description of the routines making up this program are included as Appendix C to this dissertation.

4.2. Operating Results

Three sample problems were used in developing and testing this heuristic procedure: an eleven element problem taken from Jackson (16), the twenty-one element problem used as an example in Chapter 3, taken from Mitchell (20), and a seventy element problem representing actual appliance industry data. All three are depicted in Appendix A. Although these few cases do not completely test the method's general validity, we can observe some interesting measures of performance.[1]

All three problems were processed by Phase I and Phase II of the assembly line balancing program. The twenty-one element problem was solved for five different cycle times to indicate the effect of cycle time variation on effort. Data summarizing these problem-solving exercises are given in Table 1. Appendix B includes the problem-solving protocols for each run.

Numerous additional hand simulations of the Phase II routine on the seventy element problem with various cycle times have also been performed.

Note the increase in computing effort with problem size for both Phase I and Phase II. We also observe for the several cases of the twenty-one element problem an increase in effort per station as per cent of available time used decreases. Most of the effort is spent in finding appropriate transfers for restructuring the tree. For example, in the seventy element problem, 80 per cent of the effort occurred in the regrouping generators and in carrying out the transfers they suggested.

It appears that the amount of effort required to reach a balance, starting from the output of Phase I, depends upon the number of stations desired and the per cent of available time

---

[1] It is necessary to test this procedure against other large problems not only to measure its economic efficiency but also to insure that the heuristics incorporated here have not unconsciously been adapted to meet the requirements of these particular test problems.

TABLE 1

Problem	Phase I	Phase II					
	Effort IPL Instr.	Cycle Time	Pct Usable	No. of Stations	Pct Idle	Effort[a]	Effort Per Station × 10³
11 element	14,478	10	95	5	8	153,075	30.6
21 element	51,386	20	90	6	12	141,868	23.7
		19	95	6	8	143,183	23.8
		14	95	8	6	627,809	78.5
		18	98	6	3	483,458	80.5
		21	100	5	0	760,803	152.2
70 element	207,194	176	93	23	9	2,495,118	108.5

[a] Number of IPL instructions executed.

actually used. This data is depicted in Figure 9. Additional experience with actual problems will enable us to develop a method of estimating this relationship.

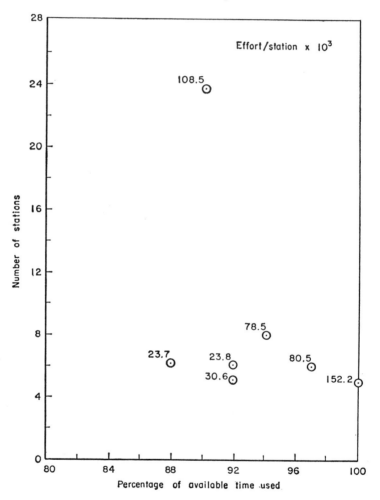

Fig. 9. Effort as a function of the number of stations and per cent of idle time

4.3. Other Comparisons

To get some feeling for the effort required by exhaustive algorithms, we also attempted the eleven element problem with only the "exhaustive grouping" generator, thus solving the problem using Jackson's algorithm (16). This is only a rough comparison, since the algorithm is carried out here using list processes entirely and would benefit more than the heuristic program as a whole from the use of matrix representation. Also, since the method is imbedded in the midst of our procedure, some amount of processing, not required by that algorithm per se, is included in the measure. Under these conditions the program required about 389,000 IPL instructions to reach a balance, a factor of 2.5 over the heuristic approach. Although this difference is not striking in light of the warnings made above, the disparity will grow rapidly with increasing problem size.

We also tested Salveson's (30) linear programming formulation on our eleven element problem, using the RAND Simplex code. The problem required eleven equations in sixty-two unknowns (one unknown for each possible legal grouping of elements, given a cycle time of ten). The code required fifteen iterations (starting from an artificial basis) to reach an optimum. As was expected, this answer contained both overlapping sets of groupings and fractional parts of groupings. Three additional constraints are needed to eliminate the intergrouping infeasibilities. We must await an operating integer programming code in order really to test the efficiency of this linear programming approach.

We have an industrial engineer's balance for the seventy element problem, cycle time 176, requiring twenty-seven workmen. (Producing this balance took about eight hours.) However, direct comparison with the twenty-three men balance found by the heuristic program is not possible, since the industrial engineer's balance took into account the zoning constraint. A quick hand adjustment of the program's completed balance, removing violations of the zoning constraint, took less than twenty minutes and resulted in three new stations, for a total of twenty-six workers. We can expect the revised program to do even better in many cases, considering zoning from the start.

To test some simple arbitrary rule for assigning tasks to work stations, the following procedure was applied to the seventy element problem:

> Number the tasks from the front of the problem so that all predecessors of any task have a lower designation number than the task itself. If several choices of the next task to number are available, choose one arbitrarily. Then assign tasks to stations in increasing order of designation number, taking each time the next higher numbered task meeting the zoning and cycle time constraints.

The seventy element problem used here is numbered in this way. For that problem, without zoning, this assignment resulted in twenty-four work stations, and with zoning, twenty-six. In this limited test, this simple rule does almost as well as our heuristic program—and probably almost as well as an optimizing procedure also. However, the saving of one worker on a balance used for two weeks would pay for the additional cost of the heuristic method.

A similar comparison was made, for all cycle times mentioned of the eleven and twenty-one element problems, between the heuristic line balancing procedure and the ranked positional weight technique of Helgeson and Bernie (12). Except for the twenty-one element problem, cycle time twenty, the later method produced balances requiring one more man than did the heuristic procedure.

Note, in viewing these comparisons, that the heuristic program's effort includes completely restructuring the problem tree, rather than just naming the components when a work station is identified. This restructured tree can be used, in place of the Phase I output, as a start in balancing the line to a nearby cycle time. Using the balance for cycle time eighteen as input to balance to cycle time nineteen (twenty-one element problem) would result in only one transfer, with less than one-quarter the effort required when starting from scratch.

CHAPTER 5

The Assembly Line Balancing Program as a Problem-Solving Process

In this chapter we examine the assembly line balancing program within a framework for problem-solving behavior proposed by Newell, Shaw, and Simon (23). This examination, made after the program had been developed and tested, does not reflect the way in which the program was devised. It is an attempt to understand the performance of this program within a more general framework.

5.1. An Abstract Model of Problem-Solving Behavior

We briefly review those features of the Newell, Shaw, and Simon formulation of interest here.

"The maze provides a suitable abstract model for most kinds of problem-solving activity. A maze is a set of paths (possibly partly overlapping) some subset of which are distinguished from others by having rewards at their termini. These latter are the 'correct' paths; to discover one of them is to solve the problem of running the maze."

Processes common to problem-solving behavior may be classified into those which propose possible solutions (solution-generators) and those which determine whether the proposal is in fact a solution (solution-verifiers).

Associated with the nodes of the problem maze are various properties. The solution is often specified in terms of nodes having certain properties. Given some measure of the density of these required properties over the entire maze, we can seek efficient solution-generating processes that propose nodes having the rare properties of solutions. We can then test these proposals for the more common properties.

Several classes of procedures are common in heuristic problem-solving: the use of simple selection procedures to determine which solution-generating processes to invoke, the use of means-end analysis in generating proposed stations, the use of planning—solving an abstracted version of the problem as a guide in solving the full problem.

5.2. Characteristics of the Assembly Line Balancing Problem

The maze representing the assembly line balancing problem consists of all possible groupings of the problem elements, originating with all elemental tasks members of a single grouping and terminating with each a separate group. Each node corresponds to a number of groupings of tasks. If we visualize the maze as a branching tree with no rejoining paths, most nodes occur many times in the maze.

The properties of nodes in which we are interested (and in terms of which a solution to the assembly line balancing problem is specified) are:

1. The inclusion and duplication of elements in several groupings (each task shall be assigned to one and only one station).
2. The partial ordering relationships within and between groupings (the ordering constraints among elements shall be met).

3. The sum of the time of elements in each group (the time requirement for any group shall not exceed the cycle time).

4. The number of groupings (the number of stations shall be satisfactorily small).

5. The distribution of total time among groupings (idle time shall be "evenly" distributed).

We refer to these as the "single assignment," "ordering," "cycle time," "minimal stations," and "idle time" properties, respectively.

It is appropriate to inquire about the densities of nodes with these various properties over the entire maze. It is also appropriate to inquire about the ease with which nodes having a certain property can be found, since this effort also must be counted in measuring the relative efficiency of solution-generators. Although we lack numerical estimates for these densities, some accurate feeling for their relative values is possible.

Nodes with the single assignment property are rare among all possible groupings of elemental tasks. If we do not limit an element to at most one appearance in each grouping within a node, the maze has an infinite set of nodes. If each grouping is constructed by sampling without replacement, but the population replenished between groupings, the ratio between number of such groupings and number of groupings formed by sampling without replacement for the whole problem is of the order of magnitude of $n^n/n!$, or (from Sterling's Approximation) e^n. For a line balancing problem of 100 tasks, this is roughly 10^{48}. However, nodes with the single assignment property are relatively easy to generate. Sampling without replacement is not excessively more costly than sampling with replacement.

The ordering property is also rare over the maze as a whole. Even for those nodes having the single assignment property, we estimate (since the "average element" in our sample problems is in a set relationship with one-third of the other elements) that $(1/3)^{n-1}$ of the possible n element groups are consistent with the ordering constraints within themselves. And one can easily construct internally consistent groupings that, taken together, are inconsistent. However, consistent groupings (with the single assignment property) are relatively easy to generate by a simple recursive procedure.

The cycle time property is rare among the total number of possibilities and becomes rarer as the minimum number of stations increases (and the average number of elemental tasks per acceptable station decreases). However, a test for this requirement can be added easily to procedures for generating nodes having the single assignment and ordering properties.

We assert that nodes having the minimal stations property, though rare over the entire maze, are not as rare among those nodes having the first three properties. Furthermore, simple tests can indicate as a node is being constructed by grouping if it is "likely" to have this property.

We choose to view the idle time property as a subrequirement of the minimal stations property. Within the set of all nodes having a minimum number of groupings, nodes having idle time property are, by the standard of the densities mentioned above, relatively common.

This analysis indicates that, although most properties of solutions are quite rare over the entire maze we have defined, several can be relatively easily generated. Further, densities of other properties are not entirely independent of these "easy" ones. Given that we do not have the entire maze "spread out before us," but must generate nodes one at a time or in small batches, it seems sensible to produce those nodes that can be created easily—nodes with the first three properties—and work from these to find a solution.

5.3. Exhaustive Procedures

It is not surprising that the exhaustive procedures suggested by both Jackson (16) and Salveson (30) generate nodes having the first three properties of a solution and then seek a node with a minimal number of stations.

Jackson's method proceeds by generating new nodes in which one more acceptable (by the first three properties) grouping is formed from the ungrouped tasks. In fact, it proceeds in parallel down all paths determined by such nodes. Since the process stops upon reaching the first node at which all tasks are in acceptable groupings, it always finds a minimal solution. If all paths were traced out to that depth in the maze, those having minimal station property could be compared and that which best meets the idle time property chosen. Since some dominated paths are abandoned during the generation process, one of the "optimum" nodes might still not be found. The suggestion of Helgeson and Kwo (13) concerns the use of cues in choosing paths to abandon to reduce the possibility of missing an "optimum" node.

Salveson's approach consists of generating all groupings which might be combined into nodes having the first three properties and then using either linear programming or some other form of combinatorial analysis to find a combination with the minimal stations property.

5.4. The Heuristic Procedure

The heuristic assembly line balancing procedure represents a planning approach to the problem. It develops a solution plan having the single assignment and ordering properties and then varies the plan to meet the cycle time and minimal stations constraints. The plan is developed in Phase I of the heuristic program and varied in Phase II. Phase III modifies the resulting solution to obtain one with the idle time property. Though this approach also makes use of abstraction to suggest a means of solving the full problem, it differs from the variety of planning found in the General Problem Solver (24). This difference will become clear in the following analysis.

Phase I. The plan created in Phase I is independent of cycle time, that is, the same plan is used for a particular product (set of ordering constraints) over all cycle times. The plan consists of a particular path through the problem maze, constructed backwards from the initial problem statement with each element a separate grouping to the initial node of the maze with all elements in one grouping. Although it is highly unlikely that this path will lead to the solution of any given problem, it is highly likely that it will be "close to" the solution path, in the sense that from this path the solution path can be easily found. It is upon this ease of moving to a solution path that our heuristic method rests.

The planned path is "universal" because it represents the physical properties of ordering relationships and thus the a priori probabilities that certain elements will be grouped together in the final solution. Such physical properties are tightness or looseness (parallelness or serialness) of structure, "key elements" which naturally segment the problem, and so forth. Figure 10 shows the planned path for the twenty-one element problem of Figures 1 and 4.

Thus, Phase I of the line balancing procedure is a planning process. It differs from the planning heuristic of GPS, which sketches out intermittent nodes along a proposed solution path which can then be connected. Our procedure supplies a detailed path through the maze from which a "similar" solution path can be found.

Phase II. The second phase of the assembly line balancing program combines solution-verifying and solution-generating processes. Given the cycle time and having estimated the minimum number of stations, Phase II sets out to verify that the planned path is indeed a solution path. Since this is in general not true, the program is prepared to propose new paths, generated by modification of the planned path.

Since the nodes of the planned path are created respecting

the ordering and single assignment constraints, they are abstracted versions of the initial problem. The same verifying

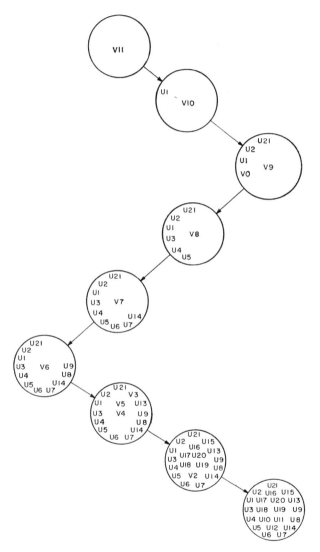

Fig. 10. Planned path for twenty-one element problem

process to be used on the initial problem for minimum number of men can be used on them. Indeed, given that the solution-

generating processes never increase the requirements for workmen (number of stations) of a grouping of elements, this verification is a necessary condition that the node is on the solution
path. Such verification is not, in theory, a sufficient condition,
but examination of actual experience using the program (see
Appendix B) shows that many times in practice it has been sufficient also. When a node on the path being traced fails this
verifying test, certain heuristics are used to produce an acceptable alternate node. These heuristics produce not just a new node
but an entire new path (quite similar to the previous one). When
a node is reached for which the cycle time property is true for
all groupings, the problem is solved. If at any stage no alternate
node can be found, the program retreats one step on the path
and begins explorations from that node.

The heuristics used in proposing alternative paths display
many of the characteristics cited earlier. Simple selection heuristics decide which solution-generating processes to try and in
what order. These solution-generating processes, the regrouping
generators, work backwards using means-end analysis. That is,
they postulate a set of groupings that would be verified and
then use their particular methods to derive these groupings.
Generally, they modify only two groupings of the set.

Phase III. In this phase, the program modifies the solution
to one including the idle time property. The same heuristics as
in Phase II are used, but now they preserve not only the single
assignment, ordering and minimal stations properties of groupings, but also the cycle time property.

5.5. Summary

We find in the assembly line balancing program the same
use of cues and of simple selection heuristics that occur in other
heuristic programs prepared to date. We also find the use of abstraction to aid in preparing a solution plan, although the nature

and use of this plan differ from that of other published heuristic programs.

Both heuristic and exhaustive approaches to line balancing use solution-generators which incorporate the single assignment and ordering constraints. A major difference between these approaches is the use of planning to find a single path through the problem maze from which to vary, as opposed to considering many paths simultaneously. Indeed, an economic comparison between the two approaches would depend on the accuracy of our minimum number of stations estimate and on how little deviation was necessary from our "ideal" path.

CHAPTER 6

Computers and the Solution
of Ill-Structured Problems

In this chapter we consider the use of digital computers in exploring and implementing decision-making procedures for ill-structured problems. We examine the characteristics of such problems, asking what is needed in the problem-solver's system of communication with the computer and to what extent current symbol manipulation languages meet these needs. In this context, we indicate how these considerations are reflected in the structure of the assembly line balancing program.

6.1. Problem-Solving and Computing Solutions

We can distinguish between use of the computer as a tool of the researcher trying to understand a complex environment and use of the computer to produce the solution to particular problems by well-known procedures. This is not a precise, clear-cut distinction, nor is it appropriate to view certain programming languages or techniques as suitable for only one of these uses. The coding and testing on sample problems of a new algorithm for the traveling salesman problem is an example of the first usage. The repeated use of this same code by a firm to schedule delivery trucks is an example of the second.

In this discussion we are concerned with the computer as an adjunct to the researcher. Eventually, when an acceptable decision procedure is found, questions of machine speed, memory allocation, and such must be faced. But while the researcher is engaged in developing these decision methods, concern with 'efficient machine utilization' is an obstacle to efficient use of the computer as an aid to *his* problem-solving processes.

6.2. Characteristics of Ill-Structured Problems

Simon and Newell (32) define the class of ill-structured problems by exclusion from the class of well-structured problems. Well-structured problems are those "described in terms of numerical variables, scalar or vector quantities" in which "the goals to be attained can be specified in terms of a well-defined objective function" and for which "there exist computational routines that permit the solution to be found and stated in actual numerical terms." They give three general characteristics of ill-structured problems.

1. Many of the essential variables are not numerical at all, but symbolic or verbal.
2. The objective function, the goal, is vague and non-quantitative.
3. Computational algorithms are simply not available.

Such diverse activities as allocating marketing expenditures among sales and promotional efforts, supplying effective logistics support to a military organization, preparing a compiler for 'business applications,' playing chess, coordinating the activities of radar operators and interceptor pilots, are all ill-structured, if not indeed perverse, problems.

The distinction between well-structured and ill-structured is often clouded. Few problems have all the properties of one class only. But the intent of the distinction is clear. It derives from the dichotomy between the real state of the world and, as von Neumann (35) states it, ". . . the fact that it is, with our habits of thought and of expressing thought, very difficult to express any truly complicated situation without having recourse to formulae and numbers." This distinction demands the attention of problem-solvers.

6.3. Heuristic Problem-Solving

Currently, researchers are studying human methods of dealing with ill-structured problems. The problem areas around which these research efforts are organized include theorem proving in geometry and symbolic logic, chess, human discrimination learning, human concept formation, and language translation. Such problem-solving activity has been called 'heuristic problem-solving' (32) to emphasize the importance of principles or rules-of-thumb that tend to discover acceptable solutions more efficiently in most cases than do exhaustive methods.

A major tool of this research has been theory-testing by construction of computer routines for simulating problem-solving behavior. This research has provided information about the nature of appropriate decision-making procedures for ill-structured problems and has led to several computer programming languages oriented toward expressing and manipulating the elements of such problems. This development holds great potential for the treatment of many ill-structured problems that arise in management. Heuristic procedures for portfolio selection (6) and job shop scheduling (10) are instances of this approach.

6.4. Information Processing Aspects of Ill-Structured Problems

Our difficulties in preparing computer decision-making procedures for ill-structured problems derive both from the nature of such problems and from the fact that we are *exploring* possible procedures. Present digital computers require an explicit statement of the procedure to be carried out and of the data to be operated upon. But at any stage in developing a problem-solving procedure our knowledge of the problem itself is incomplete. We are unable to predict the direction our problem-solving efforts will take. If we are to work freely with the computer, our methods of describing the problem and our procedure for solving it must allow easy revision of both procedures and data.

This demand for "more flexibility" is not unique to heuristic programming. Changes in procedure are an accepted fact of life in all computer programming; closed subroutine organization is the usual answer to this problem. But the usual state of affairs is uncertainty only over the details of accomplishing some function. In developing procedures for solving ill-structured problems, learning through interaction with the computer, we are not even sure what functions we will want to accomplish. Changes in data representation reflect shifts of interest in particular characteristics of the problem environment. We wish to be able to introduce new characteristics, and indeed new objects or even classes of objects, without substantial revision of the way our previous procedures are expressed.

Specific examples of these considerations can be cited in our assembly line balancing procedure. For example, we added the characteristic "zone" to the definition of an elemental task and also procedures dependent on that characteristic. We might also wish to add new compound elements beyond the Z. We desire the ability to express procedures that will work with objects of a class—say compound elements—without specific knowledge of the particular member of the class at hand. Particular features of object types should be encoded in the data and interpreted by a general routine, not specifically spelled out in each procedure. Examples of such encoding exist in present computer usage, e.g., eliminating the need to know how a number is scaled by the use of floating point interpreters and, finally, specialized hardware; the use of data file defining schemes in business compilers.

For our ill-structured problems we desire a similar ability to interpret the data, so that each procedure need not be specialized to the particular objects we had in mind when first formulating it. A chess program should not have in each routine a special section for handling pawn promotions, *en passant* captures, castling, etc. A line balancing program should not require knowledge of the structure of a Z in each routine. (The present program is not entirely satisfactory in this respect.)

Further, the nature of ill-structured problems, and of this approach to their solution, calls for procedures best characterized as networks for associating with a particular state of the problem a particular procedure or set of procedures for making some desirable incremental change in that state. In line balancing, this is the problem of choosing which regrouping generator to activate at a particular time.

Finally, these procedures often involve variable amounts of data. For example, we do not know how many compound elements the line balancing program will build up in seeking a balance, nor how many continuations the chess program will consider before a static position is reached. We must avoid excluding certain interesting procedures because their data storage requirements cannot be stated in the usual dimension specification manner.

Thus, the changing nature of data and program makes storage allocation a difficult task. And uncertainty as to how procedures will develop—an uncertainty remaining unresolved until we have made extensive use of the computer—demands the capacity for easy modification.

On one hand, we have large-scale computing equipment whose capabilities are barely being exploited. On the other, we have complex problems for which any scheme producing even a satisfactory solution quickly would be welcome. Our dilemma is that we set out to solve such problems not understanding them perfectly, but present methods of using computers require that we tell the machine what to do in complete detail.

6.5. Pre-structuring the Problem

The common answer to this dilemma is to pre structure the problem environment and then, within the resulting (often stringent) requirements, produce a solution procedure. In many cases such pre-structuring is appropriate. The problem may seem to fit or almost fit some well-known mathematical formulation. In other cases, such prejudgment of the appropriate variables for consideration and of the ways they interact is dangerous. The danger lies in the loss of flexibility thus introduced. When it becomes time to revise the approach to the problem (and it often does), the routine exploiting the problem-solver's present knowledge has been so closely related to the characteristics of the computer that he must ignore or only partially acknowledge new information about the problem environment. The natural flow of problem-solving processes cannot be freely translated into machine procedures; rather, attention is diverted to wrestling with the limitations of what has already been done.

6.6. Another Answer to this Dilemma

Another answer to this dilemma is reflected in the several heuristic programs mentioned before, including the assembly line balancing program. This answer is to build up a representation of the problem and a set of routines for dealing with the problem elements. Upon this base is constructed a set of procedures for modifying the problem in this representation. And upon *this* base the decision-making routines themselves are constructed. The subroutine approach to complex computer programs is not new. But its actual success, the degree to which it can really be carried out in practice, depends strongly on the programming language available.

6.7. Desirable Characteristics of a Language for Problem-Solving

Certain requirements for a language to express ill-structured problems are familiar to every thoughtful programmer, for translating a problem-solving procedure (even a rigorously defined algorithm) into a 'tight' running code is a prime example of ill-structuredness. These desirable features include:

1. Freedom from memory allocation problems;
2. The ability to define and redefine complex concepts, and to make use of these concepts by name in defining further concepts;
3. The ability to express concepts which are not meaningful until some problem-solving has occurred—concepts which can be made explicit only by interpretation in the problem context;
4. The ability to introduce useful local notation;
5. The ability to associate information in an easily recoverable manner;
6. The ability to change sections of the decision process independently without problems of interrelations with other sections.

These features also appeal to the non-computer-oriented problem-solver who would like to specify to the machine, in the context of what he has already told it, his latest ideas, heuristics, and decision processes for the problem at hand. We desire a language for problem specification in which decision policies themselves are the natural parameters.

6.8. Characteristics of Symbol Manipulation Languages

A number of similar computer languages have been developed which begin to provide some of this desired freedom. The IPL series (21, 26, 27, 28), LISP (18), FORTRAN List Processing Language (9), and COMIT (37) exemplify this approach to computer utilization. We refer in the following to specific features of the IPL series. The general points we make are valid, to a greater or lesser extent, for any of these languages.

The pertinent features of the IPL's are:

1. Organization of storage into list structures, so that the association of one cell with another as "next" (normally done by adding one to the machine address) is arbitrary and at the command of the program;

2. Use of description processes to associate with structures new information or to delete previously associated information;

3. Hierarchical nature of control, allowing both for a natural hierarchical organization and specification of processes and for recursive definition of processes—that is, for processes defined in terms of themselves;

4. Together with 3, facility for handling working storage within each routine so that its subroutines (including itself, if recursive) will not disturb that storage—each process is automatically a closed subroutine and, within the definition of its inputs and outputs, can be changed at will.

Taken together, these features allow the problem-solver, at some cost in processing speed, to proceed without being involved immediately in intolerable problems of storage assignment and program planning. Although none of these systems are "the answer" to the problems raised earlier, they are a first step in freeing the problem-solver from the onerous details of machine utilization.

6.9. The Assembly Line Balancing Problem

Assembly line balancing is an ill-structured problem. Some of the variables are numerical (cycle time, operation time per unit); others are not (groupings of elements). The goal is not always a simple numerical function. Each statement of the problem by a different organization contains somewhat different constraints, criteria for a successful solution, etc. Thus, the goal may be stated as a minimization of the number of workers but with an even distribution of work among the men used. The payoff may have several components, not necessarily simply related. Further, those exhaustive algorithms applicable to even a simplified version of the problem require extremely large amounts of time and/or storage for interesting cases (sixty or more elements).

6.10. Mechanizing the Assembly Line Balancing Procedure

This assembly line balancing procedure is coded in IPL-IV, an interpretive system mechanized on The RAND Corporation's JOHNNIAC. The following remarks apply equally to IPL-V, a similar language for the IBM 650, 704, 709, and 7090.

Rather than describe this routine completely, we attempt to indicate the programming philosophy by presenting a few selected details. The reader can measure for himself the extent this approach has shifted emphasis from machine characteristics to the problem itself. The two areas we discuss are the representation of problem data in storage and the hierarchical organization of the program (that is, the levels of vocabulary developed).

Structure of Data in Storage. Our approach was to code the entire process in IPL, thus avoiding most decisions about storage allocation for data.

IPL-IV provides a set of primitive description processes by which one can link information with a given piece of data. In particular, with any list is associated its description list, made up of alternate attribute-value pairs. These values may be other pieces of problem data, the names of lists, and so forth. IPL primitives exist to assign an attribute and its value, delete an attribute and its value, or find the present value of an attribute.

In the line balancing program an element is represented as

a list with its associated attributes. The structure of a particular elemental task is indicated in Figure D1.

During processing, the relations between elements are determined by exploring the network of elements indicated by these descriptions. As elements are created or regrouped, the values of these descriptions are modified. The only limit on the number of elements that can be created and on how they can be combined is the total available space in the machine.

Hierarchy of Processes. The processes comprising the assembly line balancing program are divided into several levels of vocabulary. Each level is built upon those below it. The following levels exist:

1. JOHNNIAC machine code.

2. The basic IPL package, including the interpreter and elementary processes for symbol and list structure manipulation.

3. A set of processes for dealing with data (task elements) by finding and altering their properties (many of these are simple description processes, others are more complicated).

4. Basic routines for manipulating information in the format of this problem, including some general list manipulation operations not among the basic IPL set.

5. A set of processes collectively called "the scanner," for examining specified areas of the problem structure and producing elements eligible for transfer according to given parameters (direction and magnitude of transfer). The regrouping generators mentioned next rest on this foundation.

6. A set of parallel routines that generate regroupings of the elemental tasks to result in (at first analysis) solvable subproblems. By "parallel" we mean that these routines can be left (after they have proposed a regrouping, for example) and reactivated at any later time—they sit off to one side and "remember where they were" with each user.

7. Rebuilding routines for actually modifying the grouping of task elements.

8. The problem-solving procedures—the top-level recursive routines for each phase—that evaluate the problem, request regroupings of specific characteristics, evaluate these regroupings in a broader context, and implement them, finally setting up smaller subproblems to which they themselves can be applied (as a final evaluation of the regrouping, as it were).

The introduction with this organization of the code of a new top-level procedure (the *interesting* part of the problem) generally requires few additions to lower level languages. Attention is focused on expressing this new procedure in a problem language already complete.

6.11. A First Evaluation of this Project

Let us inquire how easily this program can be (and has been) modified to reflect changes in approach to the line balancing problem, how well it does its job, and how long it took to produce.

The results, vis-à-vis ease of change, are most satisfying. Complete revisions of the criteria governing which subproblems are considered, or which regrouping procedures are used, and even the introduction of new regrouping procedures (given the more basic vocabularies mentioned above) have required a few hours or less. Even the introduction of a totally new constraint into the problem, that of physical zones along the assembly line within which tasks must be performed, appears from hand-simulation to require few modifications in the existing routine.

The program balances a representative industrial problem of some seventy elements in four hours of JOHNNIAC time. This figure is acceptable for a research-oriented approach in which machine speed was sacrificed for convenience of expression at every turn. The same routine in IPL-V on the IBM 704 would take approximately one hour; for the 7090, about ten minutes.

Now that limits on the number of compound elements created during problem-solving have been suggested by experience, the relationships between elements could be represented in matrix form and manuipulated in machine code, resulting in further savings in running time.

It is difficult to measure the effort required to produce this running routine, both because of other simultaneous related projects and because of the concurrent development of the IPL system itself. (Allocating joint costs is always difficult.) An estimate of one-plus man years seems right, starting from an initial knowledge of the problem with no ideas as to a problem-solving procedure.

With the assembly line balancing routine an accomplished fact, we can visualize possibly coding it in a more machine-like language, but just knowing the problem situation, such an approach seems almost impossible. Without some symbol manipulation-oriented language in which to frame our plans, we would never have attempted mechanizing a line balancing procedure such as this.

6.12. A Final Remark

In this chapter we have emphasized symbol manipulation languages as an aid to the human problem-solver. Another problem-solver we wish to aid is the intelligent machine. By an intelligent machine (or computer routine) we mean one capable of interpreting and reacting to some complex environment. It seems likely that such a device would proceed, even as you and I, not by going directly from complex situation to complex reaction but by proposing in the large, and then evaluating in detail, various schemes of action.

CHAPTER 7

In Conclusion

In this chapter we comment briefly on several aspects of the present status of the line balancing program.

7.1. Uses of the Line Balancing Program

We can suggest several uses of the present line balancing program:

1. Straightforward generation of balances, as described above;
2. Evaluation of the reduction of effort to find a balance when starting Phase II from a completed nearby balance as opposed to starting from the Phase I output;
3. Development of approximations to the labor-output function for final assembly by finding smoothed balances at various levels of production;
4. Evaluation of the worth, as measured by a revised labor-output function, of proposed local changes in product design or manufacturing method;
5. Provision of a benchmark, both for cost and for computing effort, against which to evaluate changes in the program itself.

7.2. Further Development of this Program

The program can be modified both to do its job better and to test additional concepts of program and data organization.

We have discussed earlier the possibility of manipulating in machine language a more compact representation of the problem structure. For example, we can add a matrix representation of the precedence relationships and check each proposed regrouping by modifying that matrix and testing for contradictions [see Marimont (19)]. Our present program can then be viewed as working with a rough representation of the problem, finding changes in that representation which are checked against the exact problem. This role is similar to that of the diagram computer in the Geometry Machine (8).

One new way of representing the problem-solving process that should be explored is symbolizing as actual data such concepts as "modifications of the problem tree." The various routines would then interpret this data to determine the appropriate behavior.

The representation of allowable complex elements as distinct concepts—thus removing knowledge of the particular properties of chains, sets, and Z's from the routines manipulating these complex elements—should also be explored.

With the vocabulary we have built up for the assembly line balancing it will be possible to express and test some of the other possible line balancing heuristics mentioned in Chapter 3. However, our present symbol manipulation languages still are too machine-like to allow this expression as easily as we would prefer, that is, as easily as we can precisely express the procedures in English.

Finally, we can consider the possibility of incorporating some form of learning into the selection of regrouping heuristics in a particular situation. A learning routine working with our present line balancing program could possess means of measuring particular problems (or, better still, basic operations from which to construct measures). We could allow this routine to gain line balancing experience either through solving a large number of problems or through solving each of a smaller number of problems several ways. We would ask that such a routine determine both which measures are useful to discriminate between problems and which heuristics tend to require less computing effort given certain values of the relevant measures.

7.3. Implications for Other Combinatorial Problems

The line balancing program cannot be used "as is" to solve other combinatorial problems. Indeed, this is not the way we would hope to profit from the experience gained in constructing this program. What we desire is a sufficiently powerful way of expressing our thoughts to the computer that we can develop procedures for new problems and observe their implications in hours rather than months. Our experience in constructing the line balancing program should contribute both to developing this more powerful computer language and to suggesting new decision-making procedures.

Further, not all abstractly similar combinatorial problems are similar in practice. J. R. Jackson points out that although assembly line balancing and job shop scheduling appear to be closely related sequencing problems, in reality they are quite different. It makes sense to expend effort seeking a good sequence of jobs for the line balancing problem, because that sequence will indeed be kept for the product run. But in job shop scheduling, the important problem is keeping the machine facilities busy today, rather than developing some optimal sequence of what to do over time. Expeditors and new jobs change the data radically from day to day, and so degrade the usefulness of yesterday's "optimum." And re-computing each day is extremely expensive.

Among the problems that are similar to assembly line balancing, and to which the type of aggregative procedure developed here might be applied with few modifications, are the classroom or conference scheduling problem and the personnel and equipment assignment problem. In these problems, the actual variations in data might be sufficiently small that an "ideal" solution could easily be varied to meet them.

7.4. Summary

The aims of this research are broader than just trying to produce a method for balancing assembly lines. We set out to test the feasibility of a heuristic approach to a particular industrial decision and to examine the use of information processing languages in implementing such an approach. As always, many interesting questions remain as yet unanswered. But based on the experience reported in this paper, we conclude that the combination of a heuristic approach and these methods of computer utilization is a useful research tool for treating complex industrial management problems.

Our present heuristic program is more costly per balance produced than an industrial engineer. (But extrapolations of even this strictly list processing program to the IBM 7090 indicate comparable costs.) But a complete evaluation of the method must also consider (1) the possibility of fewer men required along the line on the average (a saving of one man for two weeks will pay for even our present, research-oriented code), (2) the value to management of quick balances at a number of production rates, and (3) the value of releasing industrial engineers to other analytic work. And much more economical programs can now be built in the same pattern as our present code. Clearly this approach has economic merit.

Also, our experience confirms the position that present symbol manipulation languages, while a great advance for our purposes over conventional programming techniques, are still quite primitive. Much of the effort in preparing this program was expended in machine-oriented aspects of communicating the problem-solving procedure to the computer. Further research in this area is needed before the problem-solver will be free to expend his effort primarily on developing satisfactory solution techniques, using the computer as a tool for spelling out the implications of his procedures.

SAMPLE PROBLEMS

This appendix includes the three sample problems used in developing and testing this heuristic program for assembly line balancing: an eleven element problem taken from Jackson (16), a twenty-one element problem taken from Mitchell (20), and a seventy element problem representing actual appliance industry data.

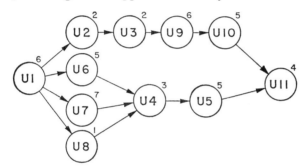

Fig. A1. Eleven element problem

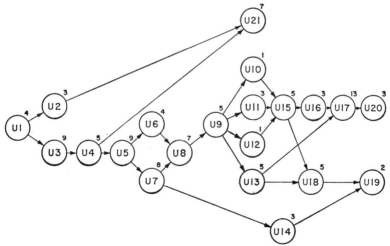

Fig. A2. Twenty-one element problem

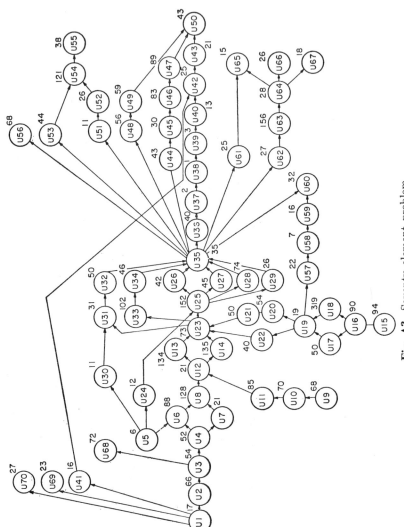

Fig. A3. Seventy element problem

TABLE A1. ELEMENT ZONES

Twenty-one Element Problem Zone	Elemental Tasks
1	U1, U2, U3, U4, U5, U7, U8, U21
3	U3, U4, U6, U7, U8, U9, U10, U11, U12, U13, U15, U16, U18
4	U13, U14, U15, U16, U17, U18, U19, U20

Seventy Element Problem Zone	Elemental Tasks
1	U1, U2, U3, U4, U5, U6, U7, U41, U68, U69, U70
2	U12, U14, U23, U24, U25, U26, U27, U28, U29, U57, U58, U59
3	U6, U7, U8, U12, U13, U24, U30, U31, U32, U33, U34, U35, U41, U68, U69
4	U36, U37, U38, U39, U40, U57, U58, U59, U60, U61, U62, U63, U64, U65, U66, U67
5	U35, U37, U38, U39, U40, U41, U42, U43, U44, U45, U46, U47, U48, U49, U50, U51, U52, U53, U54, U55, U56, U61, U69, U70
6	U9, U10, U11, U12
7	U15, U16, U17, U18, U19, U20, U21, U22, U23, U57, U58, U59

APPENDIX B

PROTOCOLS OF THE PROBLEM-SOLVING PROCESS

The several protocols produced by the assembly line balancing program in solving the three test problems constitute this appendix. The following protocols are included:

Phase   I ... eleven element problem
Phase   I ... twenty-one element problem
Phase   I ... seventy element problem
Phase II ... eleven element problem ... cycle time ten
Phase II ... twenty-one element problem ... cycle time twenty
Phase II ... twenty-one element problem ... cycle time nineteen
Phase II ... twenty-one element problem ... cycle time eighteen
Phase II ... twenty-one element problem ... cycle time fourteen
Phase II ... twenty-one element problem ... cycle time twenty-one
Phase II ... seventy element problem ... cycle time one hundred seventy-six
Phase III ... twenty-one element problem ... cycle time twenty [1]

Also included, for Phases I and II of the twenty-one element problem, cycle time twenty, are sections of more complete protocols.

Phase I—Eleven Element Problem
1 Propose chain U1
  2 Propose set U2, U6, U7, U8
    3 Define set V0 = U6, U7, U8

---

[1] Hand-simulation.

68

```
  3 Propose chain V0
      4 Define chain V1 = V0, U4, U5
      4 Cannot reduce V1 to U11
  3 Propose chain U2
      4 Define chain V2 = U2, U3, U9, U10
      4 Cannot reduce V2 to U11
  3 Define set V3 = V1, V2
2 Propose chain V3
  3 Define chain V4 = V3, U11
2 Define chain V5 = U1, V3, U11
```

The following is the first part of a parallel protocol to that produced by the line balancing program, except that it records the progress of a less taciturn problem-solver. The aim of this inclusion is to make clearer the meaning of the machine protocols. Consider that the problem-solver is looking at, and modifying, Figure 1.

Phase I—Twenty-one Element Problem

1 There is only one element at the front (U1), so let's try to build up a chain starting with U1. Since it has two followers, we'll first have to combine them into a single element.

  2 Now we are trying to combine U2 and U3 into a single compound element, a set. But since they don't have the same direct followers, we'll first set up and solve the subproblems of reducing each one separately down to the place where they do.

    3 First we'll try to build a chain starting with U2.

      4 But we don't get very far. The next element (U21) has another predecessor beside U2, and so we can't continue.

    3 Next we'll try to build a chain starting with U3.

      4 This time we have a little progress. U3's single follower, U4, has no other predecessors, so we can define a chain (V0) consisting of those two elements. But V0 has several followers.

      4 In order to continue our chain, we have to combine V0's two followers (U5 and U21) into a single element, a set.

        5 We don't get very far here either. U21 has a predecessor beside that leading to this subproblem (V0), and so cannot be reduced.

    3 Since both of our subproblems, reducing U2 and V0, have resulted in a common failure (U21), we can try to combine them into a Z, of which they are the front elements. The two back elements will be compound elements starting with U21 and U5; so to complete the Z we must combine the assemblages starting with those two into single elements.

      4 First let's take U21. Since it has no followers, nothing needs to be done.

      4 Next let's try a chain starting with U5. Since U5 has several followers, we'll first have to combine them into a set.

        5 We would like to combine U6 and U7 into a set, but since they do not have exactly the same followers, we must first treat each one separately.

          6 First we'll try a chain starting with U6.

            7 But U6's only follower, U8, has another predecessor.

          6 Next we'll try a chain starting with U7.

            7 U7 has two followers, so we first must solve the subproblem of combining those followers into a set.

              8 But one of the followers (U8) has another predecessor beside U7, so again we must stop.

Phase I—Twenty-one Element Problem
1 Propose chain U1
  2 Propose set U2, U3
    3 Propose chain U2
      4 Cannot reduce U2 to U21
    3 Propose chain U3
      4 Define chain V0 = U3, U4
      4 Propose set U5, U21
        5 Cannot reduce U21
    3 Propose Z V0, U2
      4 Propose chain U21
      4 Propose chain U5
        5 Propose set U6, U7
          6 Propose chain U6
            7 Cannot reduce U6 to U8
          6 Propose chain U7
            7 Propose set U8, U14
              8 Cannot reduce U8
          6 Propose Z U7, U6
            7 Delete constraint U14 to U19
            7 Propose chain U8
              8 Define chain V1 = U8, U9
              8 Propose set U10, U11, U12, U13
                9 Define set V2 = U10, U11, U12
                9 Propose chain V2
                  10 Define chain V3 = V2, U15
                  10 Propose set U16, U18
                    11 Cannot reduce U18
                9 Propose chain U13
                  10 Propose set U17, U18
                    11 Cannot reduce U17
                    11 Cannot reduce U18
                9 Propose Z U13, V3
                  10 Delete constraint U13 to U17
                  10 Propose chain U18
                    11 Define chain V4 = U18, U19
                  10 Propose chain U16
                    11 Define chain V5 = U16, U17, U20
                  10 Define Z V6 = U13, V4, V3, V5
              8 Propose chain V6
              8 Define chain V7 = U8, U9, V6
            7 Propose chain U14
             7 Define Z V8 = U6, V7, U7, U14
        5 Propose chain V8
        5 Define chain V9 = U5, V8
      4 Define Z V10 = U2, U21, V0, V9

2 Propose chain V10
2 Define chain V11 = U1, V10
Phase I—Seventy Element Problem
1 Propose set U1, U5, U9, U15
  2 Propose chain U1
    3 Propose set U2, U41, U69, U70
      4 Define set V0 = U69, U70
      4 Propose chain V0
      4 Propose chain U2
        5 Define chain V1 = U2, U3
        5 Propose set U4, U68
          6 Propose chain U4
            7 Propose set U6, U7
              8 Cannot reduce U6
          6 Propose chain U68
      4 Propose chain U41
        5 Cannot reduce U41 to U42
  2 Propose chain U5
    3 Propose set U6, U24, U30
      4 Cannot reduce U6
  2 Propose chain U9
    3 Define chain V2 = U9, U10, U11
    3 Cannot reduce V2 to U12
  2 Propose chain U15
    3 Define chain V3 = U15, U16
    3 Propose set U17, U18
      4 Define set V4 = U17, U18
    3 Propose chain V4
      4 Define chain V5 = V4, U19
      4 Propose set U20, U22, U57
        5 Propose chain U20
          6 Define chain V6 = U20, U21
          6 Cannot reduce V6 to U23
        5 Propose chain U22
          6 Cannot reduce U22 to U23
        5 Propose chain U57
          6 Define chain V7 = U57, U58, U59
          6 Cannot reduce V7 to U60
        5 Define set V8 = V6, U22
        5 Propose chain V8
          6 Cannot reduce V8 to U23
        5 Propose chain V7
          6 Cannot reduce V7 to U60
    3 Define chain V9 = U15, U16, V4, U19
  2 Propose Z U5, U1

3 Delete constraint U1 to U41
3 Delete constraint U1 to V0
    4 Delete constraint U1 to U69
    4 Delete constraint U1 to U70
3 Delete constraint V1 to U68
    4 Delete constraint U3 to U68
3 Propose chain U1
    4 Define chain V10 = U1, U2, U3, U4
    4 Proposed set U6, U7
        5 Cannot reduce U6
3 Delete constraint U5 to U24
3 Delete constraint U5 to U30
3 Propose chain U6
    4 Cannot reduce U6 to U8
3 Propose chain U7
    4 Cannot reduce U7 to U8
3 Define Z V11 = U5, U6, V10, U7
2 Propose chain U41
  3 Cannot reduce U41 to U42
2 Propose chain V0
2 Propose chain U68
2 Propose chain U30
  3 Cannot reduce U30 to U31
2 Propose chain U24
  3 Cannot reduce U24 to U25
2 Propose chain V11
  3 Define chain V12 = V11, U8
  3 Cannot reduce V12 to U12
2 Propose chain V2
  3 Cannot reduce V2 to U12
2 Propose chain V9
  3 Propose set V7, V8
    4 Propose chain V7
        5 Cannot reduce V7 to U60
    4 Propose chain V8
        5 Cannot reduce V8 to U23
2 Define set V13 = V12, V2
2 Propose chain V13
  3 Define chain V14 = V13, U12
  3 Propose set U13, U14
    4 Define set V15 = U13, U14
  3 Propose chain V15
    4 Cannot reduce V15 to U23
  3 Define chain V16 = V13, U12, V15
2 Propose chain U41

3 Cannot reduce U41 to U42
2 Propose chain U30
   3 Cannot reduce U30 to U31
2 Propose chain U24
   3 Cannot reduce U24 to U25
2 Propose chain V9
   3 Propose set V7, V8
      4 Propose chain V7
         5 Cannot reduce V7 to U60
      4 Propose chain V8
         5 Cannot reduce V8 to U23
2 Propose Z V9, V16
   3 Delete constraint V9 to V7
      4 Delete constraint U19 to U57
   3 Propose chain V9
      4 Define chain V17 $=$ U15, U16, V4, U19, V8
      4 Cannot reduce V17 to U23
   3 Define set V18 $=$ V16, V17
2 Propose chain V7
   3 Cannot reduce V7 to U60
2 Propose chain V18
   3 Define chain V19 $=$ V18, U23
   3 Propose set U25, U31, U33
      4 Cannot reduce U25
      4 Cannot reduce U31
2 Propose chain U41
   3 Cannot reduce U41 to U42
2 Propose chain U30
   3 Cannot reduce U30 to U31
2 Propose chain U24
   3 Cannot reduce U24 to U25
2 Propose Z U24, V19
   3 Delete constraint U30 to U31
   3 Propose chain U25
      4 Propose set U26, U27, U28, U29
         5 Define set V20 $=$ U26, U27, U28, U29
      4 Propose chain V20
         5 Cannot reduce V20 to U35
      4 Define chain V21 $=$ U25, V20
   3 Propose set U31, U33
      4 Propose chain U31
         5 Define chain V22 $=$ U31, U32
         5 Cannot reduce V22 to U35
      4 Propose chain U33
         5 Define chain V23 $=$ U33, U34

    5 Cannot reduce V23 to U35
    4 Define set V24 = V22, V23
  3 Propose chain V24
    4 Cannot reduce V24 to U35
  3 Define Z V25 = U24, V21, V19, V24
  3 Create constraint U30 to U35
2 Propose chain V25
  3 Cannot reduce V25 to U35
2 Propose chain V7
  3 Cannot reduce V7 to U60
2 Propose chain U41
  3 Cannot reduce U41 to U42
2 Propose chain U30
  3 Cannot reduce U30 to U35
2 Define set V26 = V25, U30
2 Propose chain V26
  3 Define chain V27 = V26, U35
  3 Propose set U36, U44, U48, U51, U53, U56, U60, U61, U62
    4 Cannot reduce U60
2 Propose chain V7
  3 Cannot reduce V7 to U60
2 Propose chain U41
  3 Cannot reduce U41 to U42
2 Propose Z V7, V27
  3 Propose chain U60
  3 Propose set U36, U44, U48, U51, U53, U56, U61, U62
    4 Propose chain U36
      5 Define chain V28 = U36, U37, U38, U39, U40
      5 Cannot reduce V28 to U42
    4 Propose chain U44
      5 Define chain V29 = U44, U45, U46, U47
      5 Cannot reduce V29 to U50
    4 Propose chain U48
      5 Define chain V30 = U48, U49
      5 Cannot reduce V30 to U50
    4 Propose chain U51
      5 Define chain V31 = U51, U52
      5 Cannot reduce V31 to U54
    4 Propose chain U53
      5 Cannot reduce U53 to U54
    4 Propose chain U56
    4 Propose chain U61
      5 Cannot reduce U61 to U65
    4 Propose chain U62
      5 Define chain V32 = U62, U63, U64

```
        5 Propose set U65, U66, U67
            6 Cannot reduce U65
    4 Define set V33 = V29, V30
    4 Define set V34 = V31, U53
    4 Propose chain V34
        5 Define chain V35 = V34, U54, U55
    4 Propose chain V33
        5 Cannot reduce V33 to U50
    4 Propose chain V28
        5 Cannot reduce V28 to U42
    4 Propose chain U61
        5 Cannot reduce U61 to U65
    4 Propose chain V32
        5 Propose set U65, U66, U67
            6 Cannot reduce U65
    4 Propose Z V32, U61
        5 Propose chain U65
        5 Propose set U66, U67
            6 Define set V36 = U66, U67
        5 Propose chain V36
        5 Define Z V37 = U61, U65, V32, V36
    4 Propose chain V37
    4 Propose chain V33
        5 Cannot reduce V33 to U50
    4 Propose chain V28
        5 Cannot reduce V28 to U42
  3 Delete constraint U41 to U42
  3 Propose set V28, V33, V35, U56, V37
    4 Define set V38 = V35, U56, V37
    4 Propose chain V38
    4 Propose chain V28
        5 Define chain V39 = U36, U37, U38, U39, U40, U42, U43
        5 Cannot reduce V39 to U50
    4 Propose chain V33
        5 Cannot reduce V33 to U50
    4 Define set V40 = V39, V29, V30
    4 Propose chain V40
        5 Define chain V41 = V40, U50
    4 Define set V42 = V35, U56, V37, V41
  3 Define Z V43 = V7, U60, V27, V42
2 Propose chain V43
2 Propose chain U41
2 Define set V44 = U69, U70, U68, V43, U41
```

Phase II—Eleven Element Problem—Cycle Time Ten—Per Cent Usable Ninety-five

1 Consider V1—components U1, V3, U11—5 men available
  2 Activate sequential grouping
    3 Combine U1, U2, U3,
      4 Redefine chain V5 = V6, V3, U11
      4 Define chain V6 = U1, U2, U3,
      4 Redefine chain V2 = U9, U10
    3 Combine U11, U5
      4 Redefine chain V5 = V6, V3, V7
      4 Define chain V7 = U5, U11
      4 Redefine chain V1 = V0, U4
  2 Assign 1 man to V6, 3 to V3, 1 to V7
    3 Consider V7—components U5, U11—1 man available
      4 Mark V7 as work station—9
    3 Consider V6—components U1, U2, U3—1 man available
      4 Mark V6 as work station—10
    3 Consider V3—components V1, V2—3 men available
      4 Activate direct transfer
        5 Combine U7, U8, V2
          6 Redefine set V3 = V1, V9
          6 Define set V9 = V8, V2
          6 Redefine chain V1 = U6, U4
          6 Define set V8 = U8, U7
      4 Assign 1 man to V1, 2 to V9
        5 Consider V1—components U6, U4—1 man available
          6 Combine U8, V1
            7 Redefine set V3 = V10, V9
            7 Define set V10 = U8, V1
            7 Redefine set V9 = U7, V2
          6 Mark V10 as work station—9
        5 Consider V9—components V7, V2—2 men available
          6 Activate direct transfer
          6 Activate exhaustive grouping
        5 Erase V9, V8, V10
        5 Combine U6, U8, V2
          6 Redefine set V3 = V1, V12
          6 Define set V12 = V11, V2
          6 Redefine chain V1 = U7, U4
          6 Define set V11 = U8, U6
      4 Assign 1 man to V1, 2 to V12
        5 Consider V1—components U7, U4—1 man available
          6 Mark V1 as work station—10

   5 Consider V12—components V11, V2—2 men available

     6 Activate direct transfer

     6 Activate trade

       7 Combine V2, U8

         8 Redefine set V12 = U6, V13

         8 Define set V13 = V2, U8

       7 Combine U10, U6

         8 Redefine set V12 = V14, V13

         8 Define set V14 = U10, U6

         8 Redefine set V13 = U9, U8

     6 Assign 1 man to V14, 1 to V13

       7 Consider V13—components U9, U8—1 man available

         8 Mark V13 as work station—7

       7 Consider V14—components U10, U6—1 man available

         8 Mark V14 as work station—10

Work Stations

   (U1, U2, U3)—10

   (U8, U9)—7

   (U6, U10)—10

   (U7, U4)—10

   (U5, U11)—9

The following is the beginning of another parallel protocol, this one for Phase II of the twenty-one element problem, cycle time twenty. In this case the problem-solver is looking at and modifying Figure 4.

Phase II—Twenty-one Element Problem—Cycle Time Twenty—Per Cent Usable Ninety

1 The top problem here is V11, which requires 105 time units. Since each man can be assigned at most 20 time units, at least 6 men will be needed for a total of 120 time units. Since 105 is not greater than 90% of 120, 6 men seems like a good first estimate. Let's try to divide those 6 men among V11's components. U1 requires 1 man and the 5 remaining aren't quite enough to handle V10, so some regrouping will have to be done.

  2 Since there are only two subelements, direct transfer is the first regrouping procedure we will try. That means we must shift tasks totalling at least 1 and not more than 16 time units from V10 to U1. V0 just fits the bill.

    3 Now we must combine V0 with U1. Since V0 is a chain and in a chain relationship with U1, we can define a new chain including them. Since a subelement of the Z (V10) has been removed, V10 must be replaced by new compound elements having the proper precedence relationships.

      4 V11 is now a chain of the new elements V1 and V13.

      4 V1 is the new chain of U1, U3, and U4.

      4 U2 and U21, formerly in the Z, are now combined into a set, V12.

      4 Z V10 is replaced by a set, V13, made up of V12 and V9.

  2 Now the 6 men assigned to V11 can be allocated among its components, 1 to V1 and 5 to V13. We can now proceed by taking each of these components as separate subproblems.

    3 We consider V1 first, since it is the smaller. It is assigned 1 man, and so is a potential work station.

      4 Since V1 is already large enough (greater than 80% of the cycle time), we accept it as a work station.

    3 Next we take V13, assigned 5 men, with components V12 and V9.

      4 We can immediately assign 1 man to V12 and 4 to V9, and then proceed to treat them as independent subproblems.

        5 Let's consider V12 first, since it is the smaller of the two. It is assigned 1 man, and so is a potential work station. However, since it is too small (10 time units is only 50% of a station), we must examine the other unprocessed subproblems for something we can add to V12 to make it at least 90% of a station (at least 18 time units). U5 seems appropriate.

          6 We must combine U5 and V12. This will leave V9 as a chain with a single component, so we must also replace V9 by that component (V8) in the set V13.

7 V13 is now the set of the new compound element V14, replacing V12, and V8, replacing V9.

7 V14 is the set U5 and V12.

6 V14 is now large enough (19 time units) that we can accept it as a work station.

Phase II—Twenty-one Element Problem—Cycle Time Twenty—Per Cent Usable Ninety

1 Consider V11—components U1, V10—6 men available

  2 Activate direct transfer

    3 Combine V0, U1

      4 Redefine chain V11 = V1, V13

      4 Define chain V1 = U1, U3, U4

      4 Define chain V12 = U2, U21

      4 Define set V13 = V12, V9

  2 Assign 1 man to V1, 5 to V13

    3 Consider V1—components U1, U3, U4—1 man available

      4 Mark V1 as work station—18

    3 Consider V13—components V12, V9—5 men available

      4 Assign 1 to V12, 4 to V9

        5 Consider V12—components U2, U21—1 man available

          6 Combine U5, V12

            7 Redefine set V13 = V14, V8

            7 Define set V14 = U5, V12

          6 Mark V14 as work station—19

        5 Consider V8—components U6, V7, U7, U14—4 men available

          6 Add U14, U6 to waiting list

          6 Assign 3 men to V7, 1 to U7

            7 Consider U7—1 man available

              8 Combine U7, U14, U6

                9 Define set V18 = U6, V15

                9 Define chain V17 = V18, V7

                9 Define chain V15 = U7, U14

                9 Redefine set V13 = V14, V17

              8 Mark V18 as work station—15

            7 Consider V7—components U8, U9, V6—3 men available

              8 Activate sequential grouping

                9 Combine U8, U9, V2

                  10 Redefine chain V7 = V20, V6

                  10 Define chain V20 = U8, U9, V2

                  10 Redefine Z V6 = U13, V4, U15, V5

              8 Assign 1 man to V20, 2 to V6

                9 Consider V20—components U8, U9, V2— 1 man available

10 Mark V20 as work station—17

9 Consider V6—components U13, V4, U15, V5—
2 men available

  10 Activate sequential grouping

    11 Combine U15, U13, V4, U16

      12 Define chain V23 = V25, V5

      12 Define chain V25 = V21, U18, U19, U16

      12 Redefine chain V5 = U17, U20

      12 Define set V21 = U13, U15

      12 Redefine chain V7 = V20, V23

  10 Assign 1 man to V25, 1 to V5

    11 Consider V5—components U17, U20—
1 man available

      12 Mark V5 as work station—16

    11 Consider V25—components V21, U18, U19, U16—1 man available

      12 Mark V25 as work station—20

Work Stations

  (U1, U3, U4)—18

  (U2, U21, U5)—19

  (U6, U7, U14)—15

  (U8, U9, U10, U11, U12)—17

  (U13, U15, U16, U18, U19)—20

  (U17, U20)—16

Phase II—Twenty-one Element Problem—Cycle Time Ninteen—Per Cent Usable Ninety-five

1 Consider V11—components U1, V10—6 men available

  2 Activate direct transfer

    3 Combine V0, U1

      4 Redefine chain V11 = V1, V13

      4 Define chain V1 = U1, U3, U4

      4 Define chain V12 = U2, U21

      4 Define set V13 = V12, V9

  2 Assign 1 man to V1, 5 to V13

    3 Consider V1—U1, U3, U4—1 man available

      4 Mark V1 as work station—18

    3 Consider V13—components V12, V9—5 men available

      4 Activate direct transfer

        5 Combine U5, V12

          6 Redefine set V13 = V14, V8

          6 Define set V14 = U5, V12

      4 Assign 1 man to V14, 4 to V8

        5 Consider V14—components U5, V12—1 man available

6 Mark V14 as work station—19
5 Consider V8—components U6, V7, U7, U14,—4 men available
  6 Add U14, U6 to waiting list
  6 Assign 3 men to V7, 1 to U7
    7 Consider U7—1 man available
      8 Combine U7, U14, U6
        9 Define set V18 = U6, V15
        9 Define chain V17 = V18, V7
        9 Define chain V15 = U7, U14
        9 Redefine set V13 = V14, V17
      8 Mark V18 as work station—15
    7 Consider V7—components U8, U9, V6—3 men available
      8 Activate sequential grouping
        9 Combine U8, U9, V2
          10 Redefine chain V7 = V20, V6
          10 Define chain V20 = U8, U9, V2
          10 Redefine Z V6 = U13, V4, V15, V5
      8 Assign 1 man to V20, 2 to V6
        9 Consider V20—components U8, U9, V2—1 man available
          10 Mark V20 as work station—17
        9 Consider V6—components U13, V4, V15, V5—2 men available
          10 Activate sequential grouping
            11 Combine U15, U13, V4
              12 Define chain V23 = V24, V5
              12 Define chain V24 = V21, U18, U19
              12 Define set V21 = U13, U15
              12 Redefine chain V7 = V20, V23
          10 Assign 1 man to V24, 1 to V5
            11 Consider V24—components V21, U18, U19—1 man available
              12 Mark V24 as work station—17
            11 Consider V5—components U16, U17, U20—1 man available
              12 Mark V5 as work station—19

Work Stations
  (U1, U3, U4)—18
  (U2, U5, U21)—19
  (U6, U7, U14)—15
  (U8, U9, U10, U11, U12)—17
  (U13, U15, U18, U19)—17
  (U16, U17, U20)—19

Phase II—Twenty-one Element Problem—Cycle Time Eighteen—Per Cent Usable Ninety-eight

1 Consider V11—components U1, V10—6 men available

  2 Activate direct transfer

    3 Combine V0, U1

       4 Redefine chain V11 = V1, V13

       4 Define chain V1 = U1, U3, U4

       4 Define chain V12 = U2, U21

       4 Define set V13 = V12, V9

  2 Assign 1 man to V1, 5 to V13

    3 Consider V1—components U1, U3, U4—1 man available

      4 Mark V1 as work station—18

    3 Consider V13—components V12, V9—5 men available

      4 Activate direct transfer

        5 Combine V4, V12

          6 Redefine Z V6 = U13, V14, V3, V5

          6 Define set V14 = V4, V12

          6 Redefine chain V11 = V1, V9

      4 Assign 1 man to V1, 5 to V9

        5 Consider V9—components U5, V8—5 men available

          6 Activate direct transfer

            7 Combine U7, U5

              8 Redefine chain V9 = V15, V17

              8 Define chain V15 = U5, U7

              8 Define chain V16 = U6, V7

              8 Define set V17 = V16, U14

          6 Assign 1 man to V15, 4 to V17

            7 Consider V15—components U5, U7—1 man available

              8 Mark V15 as work station—17

            7 Consider V17—components V16, U14—4 men available

              8 Add U14 to waiting list

              8 Assign 4 men to V16

                9 Consider V16—components U6, V7—4 men available

                  10 Activate direct transfer

                    11 Combine U8, U9, U10, U12, U6

                      12 Redefine chain V16 = V21, V6

                      12 Define chain V21 = U6, U8, U9, V19

                      12 Redefine chain V3 = U11, U15

                      12 Define set V19 = U12, U10

                  10 Assign 1 man to V21, 3 to V6

                    11 Consider V21—components U6, U8, U9, V19—1 man available

    12 Mark V21 as work station—18

  11 Consider V6—components U13, V14, V3, V5—3 men available

    12 Activate sequential grouping

      13 Combine U13, U11, U15, U16

        14 Define chain V25 = V26, V24

        14 Define chain V26 = V23, U16

        14 Redefine chain V5 = U17, U20

        14 Define set V23 = U13, V22

        14 Redefine chain V16 = V21, V25

        14 Define set V24 = V5, V14

        14 Define chain V22 = U11, U15

    12 Assign 1 man to V26, 2 to V24

      13 Consider V26—components V23, U16—1 man available

        14 Mark V26 as work station —16

      13 Consider V24—components V5, V14—2 men available

        14 Assign 1 man to V5, 1 to V14

15 Consider V5—components U17, U20—1 man available

  16 Combine U19, V5

    17 Redefine set V24 = V27, V14

    17 Define set V27 = U19, V5

    17 Redefine set V14 = U18, V12

  16 Mark V27 as work station—18

15 Consider V14—components U18, V12—1 man available

  16 Combine U14, V14

    17 Redefine set V24 = V27, V28

    17 Define set V28 = U18, V12, U14

    17 Redefine chain V9 = V15, V16

  16 Mark V28 as work station—18

Work Stations

  (U1, U3, U4)—18

  (U5, U7)—17

  (U6, U8, U9, U10, U12)—18

  (U11, U13, U15, U16)—16

(U17, U19, U20)—18
(U2, U14, U18, U21)—18
Phase II—Twenty-one Element Problem—Cycle Time Fourteen—Per Cent Usable Ninety-five
1 Consider V11—components U1, V10—8 men available
   2 Activate direct transfer
      3 Combine U3, U1
         4 Redefine chain V11 = V1, V10
         4 Define chain V1 = U1, U3
         4 Redefine Z V10 = U2, U21, U4, V9
   2 Assign 1 man to V1, 7 to V10
      3 Consider V1—components U1, U3—1 man available
         4 Mark V1 as work station—13
      3 Consider V10—components U2, U21, U4, V9—7 men available
         4 Activate sequential grouping
            5 Combine U4, U5
               6 Redefine Z V10 = U2, U21, V12, V8
               6 Define chain V12 = U4, U5
            5 Combine U21, U20, U2
               6 Define set V14 = V8, V16
               6 Define set V16 = V13, U20
               6 Redefine chain V5 = U16, U17
               6 Define chain V13 = U2, U21
               6 Redefine chain V11 = V1, V15
               6 Define chain V15 = V12, V14
         4 Assign 1 man to V12, 6 to V14
            5 Consider V12—components U4, U5—1 man available
               6 Mark V12 as work station—14
            5 Consider V14—components V8, V16—6 men available
               6 Assign 5 men to V8, 1 to V16
                   7 Consider V16—components V13, U20—1 man available
                     8 Mark V16 as work station—13
                   7 Consider V8—components U6, V7, U7, U14—5 men available
                     8 Add U14, U6 to waiting list
                     8 Assign 4 men to V7, 1 to U7
                        9 Consider U7—1 man available
                           10 Combine U7, U6
                               11 Delete U14 from waiting list
                               11 Define set V17 = U6, U7
                               11 Redefine set V14 = V19, V16
                               11 Define set V18 = U14, V7
                               11 Define chain V19 = V17, V18
                           10 Mark V17 as work station—12

9 Consider V18—components U14, V7—4 men
available

  10 Add U14 to waiting list

  10 Assign 4 men to V7

    11 Consider V7—components U8, U9, V6
—4 men available

      12 Activate sequential grouping

        13 Combine U8, U9, U10, U12

          14 Redefine chain V7 = V22,
V6

          14 Define chain V22 = U8,
U9, V21

          14 Redefine chain V3 =U11,
U15

          14 Define   set   V21 = U12,
U10

      12 Assign 1 man to V22, 3 to V6

        13 Consider   V22—components
U8, U9, V21—1 man available

          14 Mark V22 as work sta-
tion—14

        13 Consider   V6—components
U13, V4, V3, V5—3 men available

          14 Activate sequential
grouping

          14 Activate complete group-
ing

15 Combine V3, U13

  16 Define set V23 = U13, V3

  16 Redefine chain V7 = V22, V25

  16 Define set V24 = V5, V4

  16 Define chain V25 = V23, V24

15 Combine V4, U16

  16 Redefine chain V5 = V26, U17

  16 Define set V26 = V4, U16

  16 Redefine chain V25 = V23, V5

          14 Assign 1 man to V23, 2
to V5

15 Consider V23—components U13, V3—1 man available

  16 Mark V23 as work station—13

15 Consider V5—components V26, U17—2 men available

  16 Assign 1 man to V26, 1 to U17

    17 Consider V26—components V4, U16—1 man available

18 Combine V26, U14
    19 Redefine chain V5 = V27, U17
    19 Define set V27 =V4, U16, U14
    19 Redefine chain V19 = V17, V7
18 Mark V27 as work station—13
17 Consider U17—1 man available
18 Mark U17 as work station—13

Work Stations
  (U1, U3)—13
  (U4, U5)—14
  (U6, U7)—12
  (U8, U9, U10, U12)—14
  (U11, U13, U15)—13
  (U14, U16, U18, U19)—13
  (U17)—13
  (U2, U20, U21)—13

Phase II—Twenty-one Element Problem—Cycle Time Twenty-one—Per Cent Usable One Hundred
1 Consider V11—components U1, V10—5 men available
  2 Activate direct transfer
    3 Combine V0, U2, U1
      4 Redefine chain V11 = V14, V12
      4 Define chain V14 = U1, V1
      4 Define set V1 = U2, V0
      4 Define set V12 = V9, U21
  2 Assign 1 man to V14, 4 to V12
    3 Consider V14—components U1, V1—1 man available
      4 Mark V14 as work station—21
    3 Consider V12—components V9, U21—4 men available
      4 Activate direct transfer
      4 Activate complete grouping
        5 Combine U5, U7, U6
          6 Redefine chain V9 = V18, V16
          6 Define chain V18 = U5, V15
          6 Define set V15 = U6, U7
          6 Define set V16 = U14, V7
        5 Combine U8, U21, U9, U10, U12
          6 Redefine chain V7 = V22, V6
          6 Define chain V22 = V21, V20
          6 Redefine chain V3 = U11, U15
          6 Define set V21 = V19, U21
          6 Redefine chain V11 = V14, V9
          6 Define set V20 = U12, U10
          6 Define chain V19 = U8, U9

   5 Combine U13, U11, U15, U18, U14

     6 Redefine set V16 = V28, V7

     6 Define set V28 = V27, U14

     6 Redefine chain V7 = V22, V25

     6 Define chain V27 = V24, U18

     6 Define set V25 = V5, U19

     6 Define set V24 = U13, V23

     6 Define chain V23 = U11, U15

   5 Combine V5, U19

     6 Define set V29 = U19, V5

     6 Redefine chain V7 = V22, V29

  4 Assign 1 man to V14, 4 to V9

   5 Consider V9—components V18, V16—4 men available

     6 Assign 1 man to V18, 3 to V16

       7 Consider V18—components U5, V15—1 man available

       8 Mark V18 as work station—21

       7 Consider V16—components V28, V7—3 men available

       8 Assign 1 man to V28, 2 to V7

         9 Consider V28—components V27, U14—1 man available

         10 Mark V28 as work station—21

         9 Consider V7—components V22, V29—2 men available

         10 Assign 1 man to V22, 1 to V29

           11 Consider V22—components V21, V20—1 man available

           12 Mark V22 as work station—21

           11 Consider V29—components U19, V5—1 man available

           12 Mark V29 as work station—21

Work Stations

  (U1, U2, U3, U4)—21

  (U5, U6, U7)—21

  (U11, U13, U14, U15, U18)—21

  (U8, U9, U10, U12, U21)—21

  (U16, U17, U19, U20)—21

Phase II—Seventy Element Problem—Cycle Time One Hundred Seventy-six—Per Cent Usable Ninety-three

1 Consider V44—components U69, U70, U68, V43, U41—21 men available—2 men excess

  2 Add U41, U70, U69, to waiting list

  2 Assign 1 man to U68, 21 to V43

   3 Consider U68—1 man available—1 man excess

    4 Combine U68, U41, U69, U70

    5 Redefine set V44 = V47, V43
    5 Define set V47 = U70, U69, U41, U68
  4 Combine U57, U24, V47
    5 Redefine set V44 = V49, V43
    5 Define set V49 = U57, U24, U70, U69, U41, U68
    5 Redefine set V26 = V51, U30
    5 Define set V50 = V24, V21
    5 Define chain V51 = V19, V50
    5 Redefine chain V7 = U58, U59
  4 Mark V49 as work station—172
3 Consider V43—components V7, U60, V27, V42—20 men available
—2 men excess
  4 Add U60, V7 to waiting list
  4 Assign 14 men to V27, 7 to V42
    5 Consider V42—components V35, U56, V37, V41—7 men available—1 man excess
      6 Assign 2 men to V35, 1 to U56, 2 to V37, 3 to V41
        7 Consider U56—1 man available
          8 Combine U56, V7, U60
            9 Redefine set V42 = V35, V55, V37, V41
            9 Define set V55 = U56, V52
            9 Define chain V54 = V27, V42
            9 Define chain V52 = U58, U59, U60
            9 Redefine set V44 = V49, V54
          8 Combine V36, V55
            9 Redefine set V42 = V35, V56, V58, V41
            9 Define set V56 = U66, U67, U56, V52
            9 Define set V57 = V32, U61
            9 Define chain V58 = V57, U65
          8 Mark V56 as work station—167
        7 Consider V35—components V34, U54, U55—2 men available
          8 Activate sequential grouping
            9 Combine U55, U54
               10 Redefine chain V35 = V34, V59
               10 Define chain V59 = U54, U55
          8 Assign 1 man to V34, 1 to V59
            9 Consider V34—components V31, U53—1 man available
               10 Combine U48, U62, V34
                  11 Redefine chain V35 = V61, V59
                  11 Define set V61 = U48, U62, V31, U53
                  11 Redefine chain V32 = U63, U64
                  11 Redefine set V40 = V39, V29, U49
               10 Mark V61 as work station—164

9 Consider V59—components U54, U55—1 man available .

10 Mark V59 as work station—159

7 Consider V58—components V57, U65—2 men available

8 Activate direct transfer

9 Combine U64, U61, U65

10 Redefine chain V58 = U63, V63

10 Define chain V63 = V62, U65

10 Define set V62 = U64, U61

8 Assign 1 man to U63, 1 to V63

9 Consider V63—components V62, U65—1 man available

10 Combine U50, U49, V63

11 Redefine chain V58 = U63, V65

11 Define set V65 = V64, V63

11 Redefine set V42 = V35, V56, V58, V40

11 Define chain V64 = U49, U50

11 Redefine set V40 = V39, V29

10 Mark V65 as work station—170

9 Consider U63—1 man available

10 Mark U63 as work station—156

7 Consider V40—components V39, V29—2 men available —1 man excess

8 Activate direct transfer

8 Activate trade

8 Activate exhaustive grouping

7 Combine U36, V27

8 Redefine chain V54 = V0, V42

8 Define chain V0 = V27, U36

8 Redefine chain V39 = U37, U38, U39, U40, U42, U43

7 Combine U46, U47

8 Redefine chain V29 = U44, U45, V1

8 Define chain V1 = U46, U47

7 Combine U45, U44, U43, U42, U40, U39, U38, U37

8 Redefine chain V29 = V28, V1

8 Define set V28 = V3, V25

8 Redefine set V42 = V35, V56, V58, V29

8 Define chain V25 = U37, U38, U39, U40, U42, U43

8 Define chain V3 = U44, U45

7 Consider V29—components V28, V1—2 men available —1 man excess

8 Assign 1 man to V28, 1 to V1

         9 Consider V28—components V3, V25—1 man available—1 man excess

          10 Mark V28 as work station—138

         9 Consider V1—components U46, U47—1 man available—1 man excess

          10 Mark V1 as work station—172

5 Consider V0—components V27, U36—14 men available—1 man excess

  6 Assign 14 men to V27, 1 to U36

    7 Consider U36—1 man available

      8 Combine U35, V22, U30, U36

        9 Redefine chain V0 = V51, V9

        9 Define chain V9 = U30, U31, U32, U35, U36

        9 Redefine set V50 = V23, V21

      8 Mark V9 as work station—167

    7 Consider V51—components V19, V50—13 men available

      8 Assign 10 men to V19, 3 to V50

        9 Consider V50—components V23, V21—3 men available

          10 Assign 1 man to V23, 2 to V21

            11 Consider V23—components U33, U34 —1 man available

              12 Combine U29, V23

                13 Redefine set V50 = V14, V21

                13 Define set V14 = U29, V23

                13 Redefine set V20 = U26, U27, U28

              12 Mark V14 as work station—174

            11 Consider V21—components U25, V20 —2 men available

              12 Assign 1 man to U25, 1 to V20

                13 Consider U25—1 man available

                  14 Mark U25 as work station—152

                13 Consider V20—components U26, U27, U28—1 man available

                  14 Mark V20 as work station—161

        9 Consider V19—components V18, U23—10 men available—1 man excess

          10 Assign 10 men to V18, 1 to U23

11 Consider U23—1 man available
12 Combine U21, U22, U23
13 Redefine chain V19 = V18, V7
13 Define chain V7 = V5, U23
13 Redefine chain V17 = U15, U16, V4, U19, U20
13 Define set V5 = U21, U22
12 Mark V7 as work station—163
11 Consider V18—components V16, V17 —9 men available—1 man excess
12 Assign 6 men to V16, 4 to V17
13 Consider V17—components U15, U16, V4, U19, U20—4 men available
14 Activate sequential grouping
14 Activate complete grouping
13 Erase
12 Activate direct transfer
13 Combine U9, U5, V17
14 Redefine Z V11 = V24, U6, V10, U7
14 Define set V24 = V22, V17
14 Redefine chain V19 = V16, V7
14 Define set V22 = U9, U5
14 Redefine chain V2 = U10, U11
12 Assign 9 men to V16, 1 to V7
13 Consider V16—components V13, U12, V15—9 men available—1 man excess
14 Add U12 to waiting list
14 Assign 8 men to V13, 2 to V15
15 Consider V15—components U13, U14—2 men available
16 Assign 1 man to U13, 1 to U14
17 Consider U13—1 man available
18 Delete U12 from waiting list
18 Combine U12, U13
19 Redefine set V15 = V6, U14
19 Define chain V6 = U12, U13

19 Redefine chain V16 = V13, V15
18 Mark V6 as work station—155
17 Consider U14—1 man available
18 Mark U14 as work station—135
15 Consider V13—components V12, V2—8 men available
16 Assign 7 men to V12, 1 to V2
17 Consider V2—components U10, U11—1 man available
18 Mark V2 as work station—155
17 Consider V12—components V11, U8—7 men available
18 Assign 6 men to V11, 1 to U8
19 Consider U8—1 man available
20 Combine U7, U8
21 Redefine chain V12 = V26, V8
21 Define chain V8 = U7, U8
21 Define set V18 = V10, V24
21 Define chain V26 = V18, U6
20 Mark V8 as work station—149
19 Consider V26—components V18, U6—6 men available
20 Activate direct transfer
21 Combine V22, U6
22 Redefine chain V26 = V18, V11
22 Define chain V11 = V22, U6
22 Redefine set V18 = V10, V17
20 Assign 5 men to V18, 1 to V11
21 Consider V11—components V22, U6—1 man available
22 Mark V11 as work station—162
21 Consider V18—components V10, V17—5 men available
22 Activate direct transfer
23 Combine U1, V17
24 Redefine set V18 = V10, V27
24 Define set V27 = U1, V17
24 Redefine chain V10 = U2, U3, U4
22 Assign 1 man to V10, 4 to V27
23 Consider V10—components U2, U3, U4 —1 man available
24 Mark V10 as work station—172
23 Consider V27—components U1, V17— 4 men available
24 Add U1 to waiting list
24 Assign 4 men to V17
25 Consider V17—components U15, U16, V4, U19, U20—4 men available

26 Activate sequential
grouping

26 Activate complete grouping

25 Erase

24 Delete U1 from waiting list

24 Activate direct transfer

25 Combine U20, U19, U17, U1

26 Redefine chain V17 =
U15, U16, U18, V33

26 Define set V33 = V32, U1

26 Redefine set V18 = V10,
V17

26 Define chain V32 = U17,
U19, U20

24 Assign 1 man to V10, 4 to V17

25 Consider V17—components
U15, U16, U18, V33—4 men
available

26 Activate sequential
grouping

26 Activate complete grouping

25 Erase V33, V32, V30

24 Activate complete grouping

23 Erase V27

23 Combine U4, V17

24 Redefine set V18 = V10, V34

24 Define set V34 = U4, V17

24 Redefine chain V10 = U1, U2, U3

22 Assign 1 man to V10, 4 to V34

23 Consider V10—components U1, U2, U3
—1 man available

24 Mark V10 as work station—137

23 Consider V34—components U4, V17—
4 men available

24 Add U4 to waiting list

24 Assign 4 men to V17

25 Consider V17—components
U15, U16, V4, U19, U20—4
men available

26 Activate sequential
grouping

26 Activate complete grouping

25 Erase

24 Delete U4 from waiting list

24 Activate direct transfer

24 Activate complete grouping

23 Erase V34

23 Combine U20, U19, U17, V10

24 Redefine chain V17 = U15, U16, U18, V38

24 Define set V38 = V37, V10

24 Redefine chain V26 = V17, V11

24 Define chain V37 = U17, V36

24 Define chain V36 = U19, U20

22 Assign 5 men to V17, 1 to V11

23 Consider V17—components U15, U16, U18, V38—5 men available

24 Activate sequential grouping

24 Activate complete grouping

23 Erase V38, V37, V36

22 Activate trade

22 Activate complete grouping

21 Erase V11

21 Combine U20, U19, U5, U6

22 Redefine chain V26 = U18, V41

22 Define chain V41 = V40, U6

22 Redefine chain V17 = U15, U16, V4

22 Define set V40 = V39, U5

22 Redefine set V24 = U9, V17

22 Define chain V39 = U19, U20

20 Assign 5 men to V18, 1 to V41

21 Consider V41—components V40, U6—1 man available

22 Mark V41 as work station—167

21 Consider V18—components V10, V24—5 men available

22 Activate direct transfer

23 Combine U1, V24

24 Redefine set V18 = V10, V43

24 Define set V43 = U1, V24

24 Redefine chain V10 = U2, U3, U4

22 Assign 1 man to V10, 4 to V43

23 Consider V10—components U2, U3, U4 —1 man available

24 Mark V10 as work station—172

23 Consider V43—components U1, V24—

4 men available
24 Add U1 to waiting list
24 Assign 4 men to V24
   25 Consider   V24—components
   U9, V17—4 men available
   26 Activate direct transfer

27 Combine U15, U9
  28 Redefine set V24 = V45, V17
  28 Define set V45 = U15, U9
  28 Redefine chain V17 = U16, V4

   26 Assign 1 man to V45, 3
   to V17

27 Consider V45—components U15, U9—1 man available
  28 Mark V45 as work station—162
27 Consider V17—components U16, V4—3 men available
  28 Activate direct transfer
    29 Combine U17, U16
      30 Redefine chain V17 = V46, U18
      30 Define chain V46 = U16, U17
    28 Assign 1 man to V46, 2 to U18
      29 Consider V46—components U16, U17—1 man available
        30 Combine V46, U1
          31 Redefine chain V17 = V47, U18
          31 Define set V47 = V46, U1
          31 Redefine set V18 = V10, V24
        30 Mark V47 as work station—157
      29 Consider U18—2 men available
        30 Mark U18 as work station—319
Work Stations
  (U24, U41, U57, U68, U69, U70)—172
  (U2, U3, U4)—172
  (U9, U15)—162
  (U1, U16, U17)—157
  (U18)—319
  (U5, U6, U19, U20)—167
  (U7, U8)—149
  (U10, U11)—155
  (U12, U13)—155
  (U14)—135
  (U21, U22, U23)—163
  (U29, U33, U34)—174
  (U25)—152
  (U26, U27, U28)—161
  (U30, U31, U32, U35, U36)—167

(U48, U51, U52, U53, U62)—164
(U54, U55)—159
(U56, U58, U59, U60, U66, U67)—167
(U63)—156
(U49, U50, U61, U64, U65)—170
(U37, U38, U39, U40, U42, U43, U44, U45)—138
(U46, U47)—172

Phase III—Twenty-one Element Problem—Cycle Time Twenty—Per Cent Usable Ninety (Hand Simulation)

1 Least possible high station $= 105/6 = 17+ = 18$
1 Consider V25—time $= 20$
   2 Activate direct transfer—V25 to V5
      3 Combine U19, V5
         4 Redefine chain V17 = V18, V20, V25, V27
         4 Redefine chain V25 = V21, U18, U16
         4 Define chain V27 = U19, U17, U20
1 Consider V14—time $= 19$
   2 Activate direct transfer—V14 to V18
   2 Activate trade—V14 and V18
      3 Combine V14, U7
         4 Redefine set V13 = V28, V17
         4 Define set V28 = V12, U5, U7
         4 Redefine set V18 = U6, U14
      3 Combine V12, V18
         4 Redefine set V28 = U5, U7
         4 Redefine chain V17 = V30, V20, V25, V27
         4 Define set V30 = V12, U6, U14

Work Stations
(U1, U3, U4)—18
(U5, U7)—17
(U2, U6, U14, U21)—17
(U8, U9, U10, U11, U12)—17
(U13, U15, U16, U18)—18
(U17, U19, U20)—18

DETAILS OF THE ASSEMBLY LINE BALANCING PROCEDURE

The only complete description of this heuristic procedure for assembly line balancing is the IPL-IV program that carries out the procedure. Inclusion of that program here would be desirable both because the procedure would be spelled out in *complete* detail and because those interested in the mechanics of using this information processing language would have a complete example available. However, since IPL-IV is undocumented, the burden on the reader who wanted to make use of this information would be quite large. Instead, we have included flow charts of the major routine of each phase, together with extensive additional comments.

Each subsection below describes the function of an independent subroutine, which can be varied by the user as desired. Notice that even this level of detail is not sufficient to predict in exactly what order the program will proceed and exactly what solutions it will reach. The order in which "equal" elements are treated may depend on their (arbitrary) position in storage. This order may determine the particular subproblems considered and the total effort required to reach some solution. Whether some solution will be found does not depend, in general, on such factors.

Phase 1. Constructing the Hierarchy of Compound Elements.
The major recursive routine of Phase I is depicted in Figure C1. The input to this routine is an assemblage of elements. The output is the single element into which the assemblage has been combined, if successful, or the reason for failure is not successful. The decision rules used are expanded in the following.

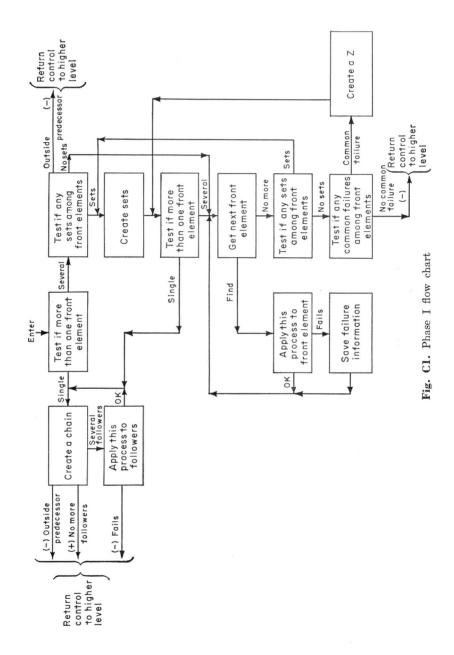

Fig. C1. Phase I flow chart

Creating a chain. Starting with a single element, the routine attempts to combine that element, and its follower, and its follower's follower, and so forth, into a chain. If some element has several predecessors, the routine fails and returns control to the next higher process with information of the other predecessors. If some single element has several followers, the routine sets up the subproblem of combining these followers into a single element (a set). If this subproblem is solved, the process of creating a chain continues. If this subproblem fails, creating a chain also fails, and control returns to the next higher process with the failure information.

Creating a set. Starting with several elements with common predecessors, the routine attempts to combine the elements into a set. If any of these elements has some predecessor other than those from which the problem derives, the routine fails, and control returns to the next higher process with appropriate information. If these elements cannot all be grouped into a single set (that is, do not all have exactly the same followers), the sets that are possible are created. Then subproblems of reducing into chains the assemblages beginning with each element are attempted. Each subproblem results in successful creation of a chain, or in some failure. When each subproblem has been processed, the routine again tries to combine the resulting elements into sets. If any elements can be so combined, the resulting compound elements are set up as chain subproblems and the cycle repeated. Eventually, all elements will be either combined into a single set or terminated by failure. If none of these elements (subproblems) meet at a common failure (that is, have some common follower), control returns to the next higher process with failure information. If there are common failures, the subproblems of combining elements with common followers into Z's are processed. After those subproblems are completed, the cycle of looking for and combining subproblems with common failures continues. If all starting elements are combined into a single set, the problem of creating a chain beginning with that element is instituted.

Creating a Z. Starting with two elements meeting in a common failure, the routine takes the two as front elements of a Z. The routine institutes subproblems of creating chains beginning with these elements and followed by the common elements at which they meet. All outside constraints that end at some element of the chain are moved so that they end at the elements following the completed Z. (This move is carried out by deleting such constraints and later, after the Z has been completed, creating new constraints.) All constraints that begin with some element in the chain and end with some element outside the chain beside the common elements are moved so that they begin with the element preceeding the completed Z. (Again the process is deletion of the constraint and, later, creation of a new one.) If the two front compound elements are now in a set relationship, they are so combined, and the routine terminates successfully. If not, the routine selects two back elements of the Z in the following manner. All common followers of the front elements are combined into a single back element, as described below. Constraints from any other predecessors are moved to end at the element following the Z. If only one of the front elements has additional followers, these followers are similarly combined to form the other back element of the Z. If both front elements have other followers, constraints leading to other followers from that front element containing the smaller number of elemental tasks are moved to begin with the element preceding the Z.

The two assemblages of elements that are to become the back elements of the Z are now combined into compound elements in the following manner. All paths from the front elements of each assemblage to the end of the problem (the total assemblage) are scanned. If no paths from the two assemblages meet (if there are no constraints between the two assemblages), each is combined separately. If one assemblage only has some path to the end of the problem, all constraints between the two assemblages are deleted and each combined separately. (Constraints coming into either assemblage from outside the two assemblages are moved to end at the element following the Z.) If neither assemblage has a separate path to the end of the problem, constraints between the two assemblages are moved one at a time in increasing order of elemental tasks unordered by the deletion until the two assemblages have only common followers. Then each assemblage is combined separately up to the common elements at the back, after which the Z is formed, and the routine terminates successfully.

Phase II. Grouping Tasks Into Work Stations. The major recursive routine of Phase II is flow-charted in Figure C2. The input to this routine is a compound element (problem), with its allocation of workmen. The output of this routine is an indication of success or failure in solving all lower level problems and, if exhaustive grouping was employed and failed, the failure information indicated below. A list of elements temporarily ignored (called the "waiting list") and the

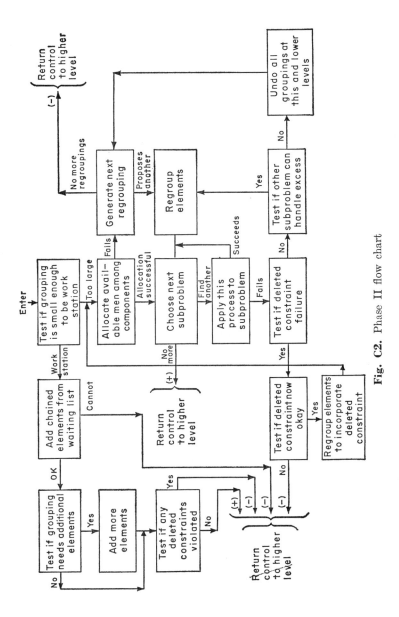

Fig. C2. Phase II flow chart

103

count of excess men available for allocation (that is, men available to the total problems but not yet allocated to any subproblem) are available to the routine at all levels and may be modified by it.

The terms "components," "subelements," and "subproblems" are used interchangeably in the following sections.

Allocation of men among subproblems. The two sources of men for allocation among subproblems are those assigned to the higher element of which the subproblems are components and those available as excess. The allocation proceeds as follows. Certain components can be ignored in making an allocation. If more than three men are being allocated and the situation is not two chained components, any components requiring 30 per cent of a station or less can be ignored, that is, added to the waiting list. The time requirement of each non-ignored subproblem is rounded up to the nearest whole man. If the number of men allocated to the higher element is at least the total of these subproblems requirements, the men are allocated and any extras added to the count of excess available. If the higher element's allocation is not enough to handle the subproblems' total requirements, excess men can be used if the subproblems' total requirements exceed three men. (If three men or less are required, excess men are not used since the regrouping procedures generally will turn up a solution.) If the rounded-up requirements for men cannot be met from either of the sources, the allocation routine terminates, signaling that regrouping is necessary (and no 'ignored' components are added to the waiting list).

Choice of next subproblem to be considered. All subproblems already processed or put on the waiting list are eliminated. Considering all subproblems now at either the front or back of the group of subproblems, that requiring the least time is chosen.

Choice of which regrouping generators to use. The following rules determine which regrouping generators are activated and in what order. For this decision, any subproblems added to the waiting list at this level and any waiting list subproblems from higher levels chained with the subproblems at this level are considered. If only two subproblems in a set relationship are involved, and neither is an elemental task, direct transfer is used followed by trading (if necessary), followed by exhaustive grouping; if one subproblem is an elemental task, direct transfer is used, followed by exhaustive grouping. If two subproblems in a chain relationship are involved, direct transfer is used followed by exhaustive grouping. If more than two subproblems are involved, and any front subproblems of the group require one man, sequential grouping is used followed by complete grouping; if no front subproblems require one man, complete grouping is used.

Operation of regrouping generators. All regrouping generators use the same basic generator to propose elements for transfer. All are parallel processes and may be reactivated to continue proposing transfers.

Direct transfer. The direct transfer generator moves elements from one component to the second so that the sum of the (rounded-up) man requirements is reduced. Transfers are considered first from back subelement to front subelement and then, if none of the proposed transfers are acceptable, from front subelement to back subelement. For a set relationship, that subelement having the most elemental tasks among its front components, components' components, etc., is taken as the back subelement. If the two subelements are in a set relationship, and further proposals of a transfer are required, the front-back order of the two elements is reversed and the sequence above repeated. No attempt is made to transfer away from a subelement that is an elemental task.

Normally the minimum amount that can be taken from one subelement and the maximum that can be added to the other define a range of possible amounts for transfer. If neither component will be a potential work station after an acceptable transfer (that is, if neither subelement is an elemental task, nor is the amount to be allocated three men or less, nor does the subelement being transfered away from initially require two men) the above sequence of transfers is generated with one-half the normal range.

That is, the range is reduced by adding one-quarter (maximum-minimum) to the minimum and subtracting it from the maximum. To propose further transfers, the sequence is repeated with full range.

Trading. The trading generator attempts to transfer some group of elements from one subelement to another in exchange for the transfer of a single large element from the second subelement to the first. The range of admissible net transfers is computed as in direct transfer. The same rules determine the order in which transfers are considered and whether one-half range transfers are generated.

The direction (back to front, etc.) indicates how elemental tasks too large to be transferred directly are shifted. Groups of smaller elements are generated for transfer in the opposite direction. The large elements are considered in an arbitrary order. Exchange groupings are proposed by the basic generator.

Sequential grouping. The sequential grouping generator first builds a station from the front of the group of components using the basic generator. This station must include enough time so that the sum of times of remaining elements can be handled by the remaining men; it must consist of more than one element; and it must include at least one of the original group of subelements. If the sum of rounded-up requirements of the remaining subelements can be met by the remaining unallocated men, the generator proposes the grouping. If not, it generates acceptable (by the same rules) stations from the back of the component group to go with the front station. If no acceptable back station can be found, another front station is generated and the cycle continued.

Complete grouping. Using the basic generator, the complete grouping generator generates a first station such that the sum of times of the remaining subelements can be met by the remaining men. Given that first station, it then generates a second station, and so forth. If at any stage such a station cannot be found, the generator terminates in failure. This method of generation is first attempted from the front of the grouping and then, if that fails, from the back.

Exhaustive grouping. The exhaustive grouping generator applies the following process from the front of the group of subelements and, if that fails, from the back. If both fail, it reports the most nearly successful sets of groupings from each direction and which elements were left ungrouped.

The method generates all independent first stations, using the basic grouping generator. For each first station, it generates all second stations. It then eliminates one of all pairs of stations containing either (1) the same elements, or (2) the same except for one or more elements in one that are in a set relationship with a single element in the other whose time is larger than their sum. For each remaining pair, it then generates all third stations, and so forth. Although this method is presently used only for two stations, it is coded in general form and can be used for larger cases.

Basic grouping generator. This is the generator used by the regrouping procedures. Its inputs are: (1) the elements from which (with their components) the grouping is to be constructed, (2) the minimum size of the grouping, (3) the maximum size of the grouping, (4) the direction of the grouping (whether from the front or the back of the input group), (5) elements to be rejected from consideration in the grouping. (Initially, all elements are considered. Elements are rejected by the basic generator itself as part of its internal bookkeeping.)

The generator first constructs a grouping from the given components less those rejected. If an elemental task is rejected, it cannot be included in the grouping nor can its followers/predecessors (depending on whether the direction of grouping is from the front or from the back). If a compound element is rejected, it is replaced by its immediate subelements. In taking elements for creating a new grouping, the largest available element is taken. An available element is one either among the initial inputs or a subelement of an input element, all of whose predecessors/followers within the input group have been taken. When an available compound element is larger than the remaining available time, it is replaced by its front/back components.

To generate further stations, the process adds the first element of this first station to the reject group and applies itself recursively to this new situation. (The routine is not coded recursively, but it behaves as though it were.) When this "subgenerator" has generated all groupings that it can, the first rejected element is restored, the next element from the first station rejected, and the procedure repeated.

To save computing effort, each new subgenerator input combination is checked to see if it is included in some already used subgenerator. Also, if the input group less the reject group is a satisfactory output grouping in itself, no "subgroupings" are generated.

The order in which equal sized elements are considered by this generator is essentially arbitrary.

As an example, consider the problem of Figure 4. With input elements (U13, V4, V3, U14), minimum size seven time units, maximum size twenty time units, from the back, no elements rejected, the basic generator would propose the following sequence of groupings: [(V4, V3, U14), (V4, U15, U13, U14), (V4, U15, U13, U11), (V4, U15, U13, U10, U12)].

Handling ungrouped elements from exhaustive grouping. If the smaller set of ungrouped elements requires more than half a station, an excess man is assigned to the grouping, if available. Otherwise, all groupings that might follow the extra elements from the back, and all those that might precede them from the front are considered. Parallel groupings are considered as both front and back. Groupings are considered in the order of back stations already created, front stations already created, back groupings as yet unprocessed, front groupings as yet unprocessed. Within each category, groupings are considered in an arbitrary order. The ungrouped elements are added to the first grouping, if any, which can include them without increasing the number of men required.

Choice of where to locate a proposed regrouping. All regroupings are accomplished by repeated application of two element regrouping. First, all elements having the same higher element in tree representation are combined. Then, the resulting elements are combined in the order they are listed for combining. If the sum of times of the two elements being combined is less than a station, and if only one of them is an immediate component of their common element (the lowest element in the tree having both as eventual components), the new compound element replaces that immediate component. Otherwise, the net change in number of chain relationships between elemental tasks is calculated for each possibility and the one is chosen that yields the greater net increase in chain relationships.

This choice procedure is overridden when increasing an already existing station or when adding ungrouped elements from exhaustive grouping to some group.

Rebuilding the structure of the tree. The new compound element replaces one of its subelements (as chosen above). The other subelement is deleted from among its element's components above. If this deletion leaves an element with a single component, that single component replaces the element in the structure. If an element is deleted from a Z, the Z is replaced by a new compound element and compound subelement having the ordering relationship of the remaining elements of the Z. Thus, if element U7 were deleted from Z V8 in Figure 4, V8 would be replaced by a set of two elements, one U14 and the other a chain U6 → V7.

Creating a work station. Given a subproblem requiring one man, creation of a work station proceeds in three stages.

1. All elements on the waiting list that are chained preceding the station must be added to the station. If these elements cannot be included without exceeding the cycle time, the station is rejected and failure reported to the next higher level processes.

2. As many remaining waiting list elements are added to the station as is possible, considered in decreasing order of time required.

3. If the station is now at least [100%-2(100%-% usable)] of a station, it is accepted. If the station is not that large, all unprocessed adjacent groupings (parallel groupings are included as both preceding and following groupings) are considered in attempting to build up the station size.

Transfers from these groupings to the station are sought according to the following rules. If any groups are chained following the station, only those groups and parallel groups are considered; if no groups are chained following, then groups chained preceding and parallel groups are considered. Transfers are attempted from chained groups (enough to bring the station size up to limit used in testing), from the other side of parallel groups (enough to bring station size up to limit), from chained groups (any transfer within the maximum limit on station size), from the other side of parallel groups (any transfer within the maximum).

Handling violated constraints. When a grouping is being accepted as a work station, all elemental tasks within it are examined for inclusion in deleted constraints. The present relationship between elements of deleted constraints is determined. If they are chained in reverse order (violating the deleted constraint), control is passed backward up the problem-solving hierarchy, at each level undoing all groupings done at that level, until the reversed constraint is removed. The two elements are then combined in a chain and the problem-solving process resumed.

Deletion of unnecessary elements. Combining elements two-at-a-time can result in chains having chains and sets having sets among their components. These redundant elements are eliminated at two times. When a grouping is accepted as a work station, all redundant elements within it are eliminated. For example, a chain which is a component of another chain is removed, its components becoming direct components of the higher chain. And when the entire problem is solved, the same elimination is performed on the resulting tree, down to but not including work stations.

Phase III. Smoothing the Resulting Balance. The major recursive routine of Phase III is depicted in Figure C3. Since this phase has not yet been coded, it is not possible to detail the heuristics it will use beyond the description that was made in Chapter 3.

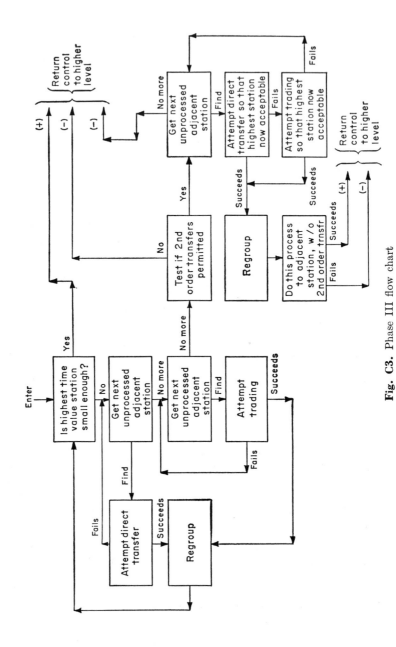

Fig. C3. Phase III flow chart

APPENDIX D

DATA REPRESENTATION

List Storage. In normal programming, storage cells are organized into larger groups by address arithmetic. The cell following cell x in a table is named $x + 1$. In the IPL system each storage cell holds both data (in IPL, a symbol) and a link to the next cell. This linkage of cells is controlled by information in storage, rather than by the computer hardware, and can be changed by the IPL program. Cells anywhere in storage (from the standpoint of machine addresses) can be linked together in lists. Information may be inserted into lists or deleted from lists merely by changing the links of the cells involved.

The power of this concept of storage organization lies in the existence of operations which enable manipulation of lists as single units. The IPL system includes such basic operations as "insert a symbol on a list," "locate the next cell after a given cell on a list," "copy a list," "adjoin two lists to form a single list." The literature on IPL-V (26, 27, 28) describes a programming system based on list storage.

Description Lists. Associated with each IPL list is a description list. On a description list the data are considered in pairs. The first datum of each pair is an attribute; the second is the value of that attribute for the list being described. The basic IPL processes for using descriptions include such operations as "find the value of a given attribute of a given list," "assign a given value to an attribute of a list." In the assembly line balancing problem the characteristics of each element are represented in description list form.

111

Representation of Elements. Figure D1 shows the elemental task U5 (Figure 1) before any processing has taken place. U5 is an empty list with an associated description list. (The cell U5 is the head of the list and always holds the name of the description list. Note that space is left in the head of U5's description list and of all sublists for the names of their description lists.)

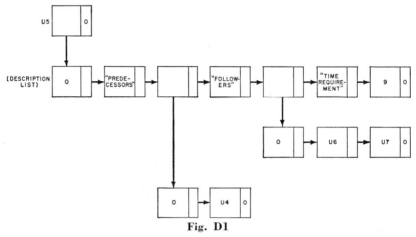

Fig. D1

Initially, U5 is described—and completely defined—by the attributes "predecessors," "followers," and "time requirement." Paired with each of these attributes is an appropriate value. The appropriate value of "predecessors" or "followers" is a list of problem elements; the appropriate value of "time requirements" is a number.

The Phase I routine determines the relationships among elements by examining the values of these attributes. As Phase I proceeds, compound elements are created. These have the attributes given above and, in addition, the attributes "type of element" and "components." The value of "type of element" can be "chain," "set," or "Z;" the value of "components" is a list of the elements that were combined to make up the compound element. Also, each component acquires an additional attribute, "above element," with the appropriate value. U5 (Figure 4) would have "V9" as the value of "element above." When constraints are removed from the problem, this information is recorded as the value of the attribute "deletions" for the elements involved.

Thus, the structure of the initial directed graph (as in Figure 1) is represented within the computer by the values of "predecessors" and "followers," the structure of the problem tree (as in Figure 4) by the values of "above element" and "components." The Phase II routine modifies the problem tree by changing the values of these attributes.

BIBLIOGRAPHY

1. Bellman, R., "Formulation of Recurrence Equations for Shuttle Process and Assembly Line," *Naval Research Logistics Quarterly,* Vol. 4, No. 4 (December, 1957).

2. Bowman, E. H., "Assembly-Line Balancing by Linear Programming," *Operations Research,* Vol. 8, No. 3 (May–June, 1960).

3. Buffa, Elwood S., "The Additivity of Universal Standard Data Elements," *Journal of Industrial Engineering,* Vol. VII, No. 5 (1956).

4. Bryton, Benjamin, *Balancing of a Continuous Production Line,* M.S. thesis, Northwestern University, Evanston, Illinois (June, 1954).

5. Churchman, C. West, R. L. Ackoff, and E. L. Arnoff, *Introduction to Operations Research,* John Wiley & Sons, Inc., New York, 1957.

6. Clarkson, G. P., and A. H. Meltzer, "Portfolio Selection: A Heuristic Approach," *Journal of Finance* (December, 1960).

7. Dantzig, George B., D. R. Fulkerson, and S. Johnson, *On a Linear Programming Combinatorial Approach to the Traveling Salesman Problem,* The RAND Corporation Research Memorandum, RM-2321 (January, 1959).

8. Gelernter, H., "Realization of a Geometry Theorem Proving Machine," *Proceedings of the International Conference on Information Processing* (UNESCO, Paris, 1959).

9. Gelernter, H., J. R. Hansen, and C. L. Gerberich, "A FORTRAN-Compiled List-Processing Language," *Journal of the Association for Computing Machinery* (April, 1960).

10. Gere, William S., Jr., *Heuristics in Job Shop Scheduling,* O.N.R. Memorandum No. 70, Graduate School of Industrial Administration, Carnegie Institute of Technology (June, 1960).

11. Gomory, Ralph, "Essentials of an Algorithm for Integer Solutions to Linear Programs," *Bulletin of the American Mathematical Society* (April 23, 1958).

12. Helgeson, W. B., and D. P. Bernie, *Assembly Line Balancing Using the Ranked Positional Weight Technique* (General Electric Company, 1960).

13. Helgeson, W. B., and T. T. Kwo, "Letter to the Editor," *Management Science*, Vol. 3, No. 1 (October, 1956).

14. Hoffman, Thomas R., *Generation of Permutations and Combinations*, Engineering Experiment Station Report No. 13 (University of Wisconsin, Madison, Wisconsin, July, 1959).

15. Kwo, T. T., "A Theory of Conveyors," *Management Science*, Vol. 5, No. 1 (October, 1958).

16. Jackson, James R., "A Computing Procedure for a Line Balancing Problem," *Management Science*, Vol. 2, No. 3 (April, 1956).

17. Johnson, S. M., "Optimal Two- and Three-Stage Production Schedules with Setup Times Included," *Naval Research Logistics Quarterly*, Vol. 1, No. 1 (March, 1954).

18. McCarthy, J., "Recursive Functions of Symbolic Expressions and Their Computation by Machine, Part I," *Communications of the Association for Computing Machinery* (April, 1960).

19. Marimont, Rosalind B., "A New Method of Checking the Consistency of Precedence Matrices," *Journal of the Association for Computing Machinery*, Vol. 6, No. 2 (April, 1959).

20. Mitchell, J., *A Computational Procedure for Balancing Zoned Assembly Lines*, Research Report 6-94801-1-R3 (Westinghouse Research Laboratories, Pittsburgh, Pa., February 26, 1957).

21. Newell, A., J. C. Shaw, and H. A. Simon, "Empirical Explorations of the Logic Theory Machine," *Proceedings of the Western Joint Computer Conference*, IRE (February, 1957).

22. Newell, A., J. C. Shaw, and H. A. Simon, "Chess-playing Programs and the Problem of Complexity," *IBM Journal of Research and Development*, Vol. 2, No. 4 (October, 1958).

23. Newell, A., J. C. Shaw, and H. A. Simon, *The Processes of Creative Thinking*, The RAND Corporation Paper, P-1320 (August, 1958).

24. Newell, A., J. C. Shaw, and H. A. Simon, "Report on a General Problem-Solving Program," *Proceedings of the International Conference on Information Processing*, UNESCO, Paris (1959).

25. Newell, A. and H. A. Simon, "The Logic Theory Machine," *Transactions on Information Theory*, Vol. IT-2, No. 3, IRE (September, 1956).

26. Newell, A. and F. M. Tonge, "An Introduction to Information Processing Language V," *Communications of the Association for Computing Machinery* (April, 1960).

27. Newell, A., F. M. Tonge, E. A. Feigenbaum, G. H. Mealy, N. Saber, B. F. Green, Jr., and A. K. Wolf, *Information Processing Language V Manual, Section I: The Elements of IPL Programming*, The RAND Corporation Paper, P-1897 (1960).

28. Newell, A., F. M. Tonge, E. A. Feigenbaum, G. H. Mealy, N. Saber, B. F. Green, Jr., and A. K. Wolf, *Information Processing Language V Manual, Section II: Programmer's Reference Manual*, The RAND Corporation Paper, P-1918 (1960).

29. Pollack, M., "Some Studies on Shuttle and Assembly Line Processes," *Naval Research Logistics Quarterly*, Vol. 5, No. 2 (June, 1958).

30. Salveson, M. E., "The Assembly Line Balancing Problem," *Transactions of the ASME*, Vol. 77, No. 6 (August, 1955).

31. Scott, James H., Jr., *Assembly Line Balancing*, M.S. thesis, Columbia University, New York City, New York (January, 1959).

32. Simon, Herbert A., and Allen Newell, "Heuristic Problem Solving: The Next Advance in Operations Research," *Operations Research*, Vol. 6, No. 1 (January–February, 1958).

33. Tonge, F. M., "Summary of a Heuristic Line Balancing Procedure," *Management Science*, Vol. 7, No. 1 (October, 1960).

34. Vazsonyi, A., *Scientific Programming in Business and Industry*, John Wiley & Sons, Inc., New York, 1958.

35. von Neumann, J., *The Computer and the Brain*, Yale University Press, New Haven, Conn., 1958.

36. Whitin, T. M., *The Theory of Inventory Management*, Princeton University Press, Princeton, New Jersey, 1953.

37. Yngve, Victor H., "A Programming Language for Mechanical Translation," *Mechanical Translation*, Vol. 5, No. 1 (July, 1958).